The Christmas Countdown Logic Puzzle Challenge

25 Christmas-themed logic grid puzzles with detailed solutions

Tarja Moles

Published by Luscious Books Ltd 2021
Morwellham, Down Park Drive, Tavistock, PL19 9AH, United Kingdom

ISBN 9781910929209

Copyright © Tarja Moles 2021

Images ©
pp. 19, 22, 46 – Igor Zakowski | Shutterstock
pp. 21, 24 Christmas tree, 32, 35, 38, 42 Christmas tree, 44, 48 stars, 53, 94 – Alexey Bannykh | Shutterstock
pp. 24 books & folders, 42, 48 sleigh – StockUnlimited

The right of Tarja Moles to be identified as the creator of this work has been asserted
by her in accordance with the Copyright, Designs and Patents Act 1988.

A CIP catalogue record for this book is available from the British Library.

www.lusciousbooks.co.uk

Are you ready for the Christmas countdown logic puzzle challenge?

Santa and his household are busy getting ready for Christmas. Festive cheer abounds as gingerbread houses are baked, Christmas trees decorated, and presents wrapped. Although on the surface everything seems under control, things don't always go to plan – especially, when there are mischievous elves around... As you go through the puzzles and work out their solutions by using pure logic, you get to find out how Santa's household is preparing for Christmas and what the elves and reindeer really get up to when Santa is not watching.

This book contains 25 challenging puzzles. You could work your way through the puzzles at your own pace, or you could use it as an advent calendar where you do one puzzle a day in the run up to Christmas.

If you're finding it difficult to solve the puzzles, here's what you can do:

1. Read the instructions on how to solve logic grid puzzles. This section gives essential information on how to get started. It also contains some more advanced tips.

2. Put the puzzle aside for a while and give your brain a rest. Come back to it with fresh eyes, and you may notice something you missed earlier.

3. Have a peek at the solutions at the back of the book. Not only will you find the answer tables with final solutions there, but each puzzle is explained step by step. Having said this, the explanations are not necessarily the only way to get to the correct answer. Depending on the order that you use the clues, you may arrive at the same solution via a different route. That is absolutely fine!

One more tip before you get started: it's a good idea to use a pencil so you can erase any mistakes you make.

I hope these puzzles will help you get in the mood for Christmas! Happy Holidays!

Tarja

PS If you'd like to send me any feedback, you can do so via www.lusciousbooks.co.uk/contact

How to solve logic grid puzzles

This section explains the basics of logic grid puzzles and provides tips for how to solve them.

What are logic grid puzzles?

Logic grid puzzles are a special type of logic puzzle where you use a grid to make deductions. Each puzzle contains the following:
* a scenario which introduces the puzzle
* clues that give all the information you need to solve the puzzle
* a logic grid which is used to record the information you gather from the clues which, in turn, form the basis for making further deductions
* an answer table where you write down the final solution of the puzzle

The logic grid contains a number of categories and each category contains a specific number of items. The items within each category are matched to the items in the other categories, but only in a way that one item in one category matches one other item in other categories. In other words, one item in one category CANNOT match two or more items in another category. This is the reason why the logic grid is organized in the way it is: all items in the different categories intersect with each other once. This allows you to figure out which items in the different categories are matched.

The basic process for solving logic grid puzzles

Here are the basic steps for solving logic grid puzzles:

1. Start by reading the scenario and the clues.

2. Record the information you derive from the clues into the logic grid by using true (✓) and false (✗) markers (you can find an explanation on how to do this on the next pages). You may not be able to use all the clues straightaway as the information included may only be useable after you have solved some part of the puzzle first. If this is the case, skip over those clues and come back to them later. You don't have to use the clues in the order they appear on the page, but you can start anywhere you like.

3. Make deductions based on the information you've marked in the logic grid and add further true (✓) and false (✗) markers.

4. Revisit any clues you haven't fully used and record further information in the logic grid. Then make further deductions until you have solved the puzzle. You may have to go through the process of extracting information and making fresh deductions several times before the puzzle is completely solved.

5. Write down your final answers in the answer table.

If you get stuck, reread the clues very carefully. Sometimes it takes more than one reading to see all the information that's hidden in the sentences. Furthermore, some clues may not seem relevant or even make sense until you have reached a certain point in the puzzle solving process. So, have patience and don't give up!

If you get really stuck, have a sneaky peek at the puzzle explanation section and see what the next step might be. However, I would encourage you to try to solve the puzzles yourself as much as possible and only resort to the explanations if you really need them.

How to use the logic grid

The logic grid allows you to see how the different items within the different categories are matched (or not). The grid consists of boxes that represent the relationships between all the different items within the puzzle. Your task is to mark each box with a true (✓) or false (✗) marker to indicate whether items are matched or not respectively. Remember that each item can only match one other item in each of the different categories.

To start adding the true (✓) and false (✗) markers into the logic grid, you need to extract information from the clues. This may sound straightforward – and it can be – but that's not always the case. It's important that you read the clues very carefully as vital pieces of information can be hidden in plain sight.

Let's look at some different types of clues, how to extract information from them, and how to mark these in the logic grid. We'll do this with the help of examples.

Straightforward true and false clues

Straightforward true and false clues simply indicate that one item is matched with another item or it's not matched with another item. Let's look at the following example which illustrates these types of clues.

Three friends each have a particular breakfast they like to eat at a specific time every morning. Can you work out what they eat for breakfast and at what time?

Clue: Mike never eats eggs or ham.
This is a straightforward statement that indicates that Mike does not eat ham and eggs for breakfast.
➤ *Put a false marker/cross (✗) in the Mike/Ham & eggs box.*

Clue: Pearl has her breakfast at 8.30 am every morning.
Again, this is a straightforward statement and it tells us when Pearl has her breakfast: at 8.30 am.
➤ *Put a true marker/tick (✓) in the Pearl/8.30 am box.*

		Food			Time		
		Cakes	Ham & eggs	Porridge	7.30 am	8.00 am	8.30 am
Name	Angela						
	Mike	✗					
	Pearl						✓
Time	7.30 am						
	8.00 am						
	8.30 am						

Whenever we put a true marker/tick (✓) in the logic grid, we can deduce at the same time that the true marker matches only those two items and, therefore, their relationships to the rest of the items within that section of the logic grid are false.

In the case of Pearl's breakfast time of 8.30 am, this means that she does not have breakfast at 7.30 am or 8.00 am.
➤ *Put false markers/crosses (✗) in the Pearl/7.30 am box and Pearl/8.00 am box.*

This also means that Angela and Mike cannot have their breakfast at 8.30 am.
➤ *Put false markers/crosses (✗) in the Angela/8.30 am box and Mike/8.30 am box.*

		Food			Time		
		Cakes	Ham & eggs	Porridge	7.30 am	8.00 am	8.30 am
Name	Angela						✗
	Mike	✗					✗
	Pearl				✗	✗	✓
Time	7.30 am						
	8.00 am						
	8.30 am						

The above deduction is an example of a simple rule that we will use in every single puzzle: Every time we put a true marker/tick (✓) in the grid, we can insert false markers/crosses (✗) along the row (horizontal line) and column (vertical line) that align with the true marker/tick (✓) within the category section. This is because each item can only match one other item within each category.

A quantitative relationship clue sounds like a bit of a mouthful, but it simply means that one item is either more or less than another item. Let's look at two examples to get a better idea of what this means in practice.

Example 1: Unspecific clue

Unspecific quantitative relationship clues don't specify the amount or degree of difference between the items. In other words, we don't know exactly how much more or less one item is in relation to another item.

Clue: The person who has cakes for breakfast eats them earlier than Mike.
This means that the cake eater's breakfast time cannot be the latest time, that is 8.30 am, because there is at least Mike – and potentially also another person – who eats breakfast after the cake eater.
↬ *Put a false marker/cross (✗) in the 8.30 am/Cakes box.*

This clue also means that Mike cannot have the earliest breakfast time, that is 7.30 am, because the cake eater – and potentially also another person – has breakfast before him.
↬ *Put a false marker/cross (✗) in the Mike/7.30 am box.*

		Food			Time		
		Cakes	Ham & eggs	Porridge	7.30 am	8.00 am	8.30 am
Name	Angela						
	Mike	✗			✗		
	Pearl						
Time	7.30 am			
	8.00 am			
	8.30 am	✗		

There is one more piece of information that we can extract from this clue:
The clue indicates that the cake eater has breakfast at a different time than Mike. This means that Mike cannot be the one who has cakes for breakfast.
↬ *Put a false marker/cross (✗) in the Mike/Cakes box.*

Example 2: Specific clue

Specific quantitative relationship clues specify the exact amount or degree of difference between items. In other words, we know exactly how much more or less one item is in relation to another item.

Clue: The person who has cakes for breakfast eats them 60 minutes earlier than Pearl.
When we look at the breakfast time options in the grid, we can see that the times of 7.30 am and 8.30 am are the only times that are 60 minutes apart from each other. So, since the cake eater has breakfast 60 minutes earlier than Pearl, the cake eater must have breakfast at 7.30 am and Pearl must have breakfast at 8.30 am.
↬ *Put true markers/ticks (✓) in the 7.30 am/Cakes and Pearl/8.30 am boxes.*

		Food			Time		
		Cakes	Ham & eggs	Porridge	7.30 am	8.00 am	8.30 am
Name	Angela						
	Mike						
	Pearl						✓
Time	7.30 am	✓		
	8.00 am			
	8.30 am			

Now that we've put true markers/ticks (✓) in the grid, we can deduce at the same time that the true markers only link their respective two items. Hence, their relationship to the rest of the items within those sections of the logic grid are false. This means the following:

In the case of the cake eater's breakfast time being 7.30 am, this means that the people who have ham & eggs or porridge for breakfast cannot eat them at 7.30 am.
↬ *Put false markers/crosses (✗) in the 7.30 am/Ham & eggs and 7.30 am/Porridge boxes.*
This also means that the person who has cakes for breakfast cannot eat them at 8.00 am or 8.30 am.
↬ *Put false markers/crosses (✗) in the 8.00 am/Cakes and 8.30 am/Cakes boxes.*

		Food			Time		
		Cakes	Ham & eggs	Porridge	7.30 am	8.00 am	8.30 am
Name	Angela						
	Mike						
	Pearl						✓
Time	7.30 am	✓	✗	✗
	8.00 am	✗		
	8.30 am	✗		

With reference to Pearl having breakfast at 8.30 am, this means that she cannot have breakfast at 7.30 am or 8.00 am.
→ *Put false markers/crosses (×) in the Pearl/7.30 am and Pearl/8.00 am boxes.*

This also means that neither Angela nor Mike can have their breakfast at 8.30 am.
→ *Put false markers/crosses (×) in the Angela/8.30 am and Mike/8.30 am boxes.*

Remember the simple rule: Every time we put a true marker/tick (✓) in the grid, we can insert false markers/crosses (×) along the row and column that align with the true marker/tick (✓) within the category section.

		Food			Time		
		Cakes	Ham & eggs	Porridge	7.30 am	8.00 am	8.30 am
Name	Angela						×
	Mike						×
	Pearl				×	×	✓
Time	7.30 am	✓	×	×			
	8.00 am	×					
	8.30 am	×					

Group clues

Group clues refer to clues that contain interlinked information about two or more items. This type of clue can take a number of forms, such as:
* *Of X and Y, one was A and the other was B.*
* *Of X, Y, and Z, two were female and one was male.*
* *The combined number of letters in the first names of people who owned A and B was ten.*
* *Neither X nor Y was A.*
* *Either X or Y was A.*

Initially these clues may or may not give you any useable information to extract. If you can put any true (✓) or false (×) markers in the logic grid, by all means do so. If you can't immediately extract any information at all, leave these types of clues until you've found out more about the items in other clues first. Remember: you don't have to use the clues in the order they appear in the puzzle. Now, let's look at some examples.

Clue: Of Angela and Mike, one has cakes for breakfast and the other eats at 8.00 am.
This clue tells us that it is either Angela or Mike who has cakes. This means that Pearl cannot be the one who has cakes for breakfast.
→ *Put a false marker/cross (×) in the Pearl/Cakes box.*
This clue also tells us that it is either Angela or Mike who has breakfast at 8.00 am. It follows from this that Pearl cannot have breakfast at 8.00 am.
→ *Put a false marker/cross (×) in the Pearl/8.00 am box.*
There is one more piece of information that can be extracted from this clue: The cake eater cannot be the same person who has breakfast at 8.00 am.
→ *Put a false marker/cross (×) in the 8.00 am/Cakes box.*

		Food			Time		
		Cakes	Ham & eggs	Porridge	7.30 am	8.00 am	8.30 am
Name	Angela						
	Mike						
	Pearl	×				×	
Time	7.30 am						
	8.00 am	×					
	8.30 am						

Clue: The combined number of letters in the names of people who have their breakfast at 8.00 am and 8.30 am is nine.
We can see that Angela's name has 6 letters, Mike's name has 4 letters, and Pearl's name has 5 letters. Therefore, the people mentioned in the clue must be Mike (4 letters) and Pearl (5 letters) – the combined number of letters in their names is 9. It follows from this that of Mike and Pearl, one has breakfast at 8.00 am and the other has breakfast at 8.30 am (but not necessarily in this order). It follows from this that Angela cannot have breakfast at 8.00 am or at 8.30 am. Therefore, she must have her breakfast at 7.30 am
→ *Put a true marker/tick (✓) in the Angela/7.30 am box.*

As explained before, whenever we insert a true marker (✓) in the grid, we can add false markers/crosses (×) along the row and column that align with the true marker/tick (✓) within the same category section.
→ *Put false markers/crosses (×) in the Angela/8.00 am and Angela/8.30 am boxes, as well as in Mike/7.30 am and Pearl/7.30 am boxes.*

		Food			Time		
		Cakes	Ham & eggs	Porridge	7.30 am	8.00 am	8.30 am
Name	Angela				✓	×	×
	Mike				×		
	Pearl				×		
Time	7.30 am						
	8.00 am						
	8.30 am						

The next clue is not, strictly speaking, a group clue, but it has an 'either – or' construction which can be present in a group clue. We'll use it to illustrate how two clues can complement each other.

Clue 1: Either Angela eats cakes or her breakfast time is 8.30 am.

This clue does not tell directly anything about Angela. However, it does hide a piece of information that we can add into the grid: Since Angela eating cakes and her breakfast time being 8.30 am are mutually exclusive – that is, they both cannot be true at the same time – we can deduce that the person who eats cakes cannot have breakfast at 8.30 am.

↬ *Put a false marker/cross (✗) in the 8.30 am/Cakes box.*

We would need further clues to continue with this puzzle.

		Cakes	Ham & eggs	Porridge	7.30 am	8.00 am	8.30 am
Name	Angela						
	Mike						
	Pearl						
Time	7.30 am						
	8.00 am						
	8.30 am	✗					

Let's say that the next clue is:

Clue 2: Neither Angela nor Mike has breakfast at 8.30 am.

This is a straightforward statement that allows us to put false markers/crosses (✗) in the grid. It also allows us to make a deduction: Since Angela and Mike do not have breakfast at 8.30 am, it must be Pearl who has breakfast at 8.30 am.

↬ *Put false markers/crosses (✗) in the Angela/8.30 am and Mike/8.30 am boxes.*
↬ *Put a true marker/tick (✓) in the Pearl/8.30 am box.*

And since we know that Pearl is having breakfast at 8.30 am, it follows that she cannot have breakfast at 7.30 am or 8.00 am.

↬ *Put false markers/crosses (✗) in the Pearl/7.30 am and Pearl/8.00 am boxes.*

		Cakes	Ham & eggs	Porridge	7.30 am	8.00 am	8.30 am
Name	Angela						✗
	Mike						✗
	Pearl				✗	✗	✓
Time	7.30 am						
	8.00 am						
	8.30 am	✗					

We can now go back to the clue at the top of the page:

Either Angela eats cakes or her breakfast time is 8.30 am.

Now that we know that Angela does not have breakfast at 8.30 am, we can deduce that she must have cakes for breakfast.

↬ *Put a true marker/tick (✓) in the Angela/Cakes box.*

We can further deduce that since Angela has cakes for breakfast, Mike and Pearl cannot have cakes for breakfast.

↬ *Put false markers/crosses (✗) in the Mike/Cakes and Pearl/Cakes boxes.*

Also, since Angela has cakes, she cannot have ham & eggs or porridge.

↬ *Put false markers/crosses (✗) in the Angela/Ham & eggs and Angela/Porridge boxes.*

		Cakes	Ham & eggs	Porridge	7.30 am	8.00 am	8.30 am
Name	Angela	✓	✗	✗			✗
	Mike	✗					✗
	Pearl	✗			✗	✗	✓
Time	7.30 am						
	8.00 am						
	8.30 am	✗					

Making deductions with the help of the grid

We have already covered the simple rule that stems from the fact that each item can only match one other item within each category. Namely, every time we put a true marker/tick (✓) in the grid, we can insert false markers/crosses (✗) along the row and column that align with the true marker/tick (✓) within the category section.

The next most used deduction method with the help of the grid is called transpositions. This means that we look at the different category sections and the markers within them, and deduce how the information marked in these sections relate to other category sections. This can be done by using logic in the following way:

If X equals Y, and if Y equals Z, then X equals Z.
If X equals Y, and if Y does not equal Z, then X does not equal Z.
If X does not equal Y, and Y equals Z, then X does not equal Z.

Let's have a look at some examples as they will make transpositions easier to understand.

Let's assume that we have already extracted some information from the clues and this is how our grid looks: We can see that Mike has porridge for breakfast, Pearl has her breakfast at 8.30 am, and the person who has cakes for breakfast does not eat at 8.30 am.

		Food			Time		
		Cakes	Ham & eggs	Porridge	7.30 am	8.00 am	8.30 am
Name	Angela						✗
	Mike						✗
	Pearl				✗	✗	✓
Time	7.30 am						
	8.00 am						
	8.30 am						

		Food			Time		
		Cakes	Ham & eggs	Porridge	7.30 am	8.00 am	8.30 am
Name	Angela		✗				✗
	Mike	✗	✗	✓			✗
	Pearl			✗	✗	✗	✓
Time	7.30 am						
	8.00 am						
	8.30 am	✗					

The most straightforward way to transpose markers in the grid is to use true markers/ticks (✓) as focal points. Whenever we insert a true marker/tick (✓) in the grid and have added the false markers/crosses (✗) along the corresponding row and column within the category section, we should next check if we can use the true marker/tick (✓) to transpose markers to other category sections.

In our example we have a true marker/tick (✓) in the Mike/Porridge box. We can also see that there is a false marker/cross (✗) in the Mike/8.30 am box. Since Mike has porridge for breakfast and he does not have his breakfast at 8.30 am, it follows that porridge is not eaten at 8.30 am.
➤ *Put a false marker/cross (✗) in the Porridge/8.30 am box.*

		Food			Time		
		Cakes	Ham & eggs	Porridge	7.30 am	8.00 am	8.30 am
Name	Angela			✗			✗
	Mike	✗	✗	✓			✗
	Pearl			✗	✗	✗	✓
Time	7.30 am						
	8.00 am						
	8.30 am	✗		✗			

Now we can see that there are two false markers/crosses (✗) on the bottom row of the grid. This has left only one box empty along that row. This means that in the empty box there has to be a true marker/tick (✓) – remember: in every category each item has to match another item.
➤ *Put a true marker/tick (✓) in the 8.30 am/Ham & eggs box.*

Since we have inserted a true marker/tick (✓) in the grid, we can next add false markers/crosses (✗) along the column that aligns with the true marker/tick (✓) within the category section. (In principle, we could also add the false markers/crosses (✗) along the row, but these markers are already in place.)
➤ *Put false markers/crosses (✗) in the 7.30 am/Ham & eggs and 8.00 am/Ham & eggs boxes.*

		Food			Time		
		Cakes	Ham & eggs	Porridge	7.30 am	8.00 am	8.30 am
Name	Angela			✗			✗
	Mike	✗	✗	✓			✗
	Pearl			✗	✗	✗	✓
Time	7.30 am		✗				
	8.00 am		✗				
	8.30 am	✗	✓	✗			

Transpositions can also be made when we can see two related true markers/ticks (✓) in different category sections. In this example, we can see that Pearl has breakfast at 8.30 am, and ham and eggs are eaten at 8.30 am. Therefore, we can deduce that it is Pearl who has ham and eggs.

→ *Put a true marker/tick (✓) in the Pearl/Ham & eggs box.*

		Food			Time		
		Cakes	Ham & eggs	Porridge	7.30 am	8.00 am	8.30 am
Name	Angela		×	×			×
	Mike	×	×	✓			×
	Pearl	×	✓	×	×	×	✓
Time	7.30 am		×				
	8.00 am		×				
	8.30 am	×	✓	×			

Again, as we have added a true marker/tick (✓) in the grid, we should check if we can add any false markers/crosses (×) along the corresponding row and column. When we look at the grid, we can see that there is one empty box along the row that aligns with the true marker/tick (✓) and another empty box along the column.

→ *Put false markers/crosses (×) in the Angela/Ham & eggs and Pearl/Cakes boxes.*

Now we can see that there is only one box that's empty in the Name/Food section: the box of Angela/Cakes. Since neither the row that relates to Angela in this section nor the column that relates to Cakes has any true markers/ticks (✓), this means that this box has to have a true marker/tick (✓) in it. In other words, Angela must have cakes for breakfast.

→ *Put a true marker/tick (✓) in the Angela/Cakes box.*

		Food			Time		
		Cakes	Ham & eggs	Porridge	7.30 am	8.00 am	8.30 am
Name	Angela	✓	×	×			×
	Mike	×	×	✓			×
	Pearl	×	✓	×	×	×	✓
Time	7.30 am		×				
	8.00 am		×				
	8.30 am	×	✓	×			

At this point there are no more transpositions that can be made. We would need a new clue to continue solving this puzzle.

Transpositions can be made in similar ways when we have larger grids. Additionally, there are more advanced ways in which we can transpose information. The larger the grids get, the trickier it can be to notice all the possible transpositions. Therefore, it's best to work methodically to make sure we don't miss anything. Let's look at an example so we understand what this means in practice.

This puzzle grid tells us the following:

Information derived from the higher gray row – in other words, with reference to the true marker/tick (✓) in the Angela/Cakes box:

* Angela has cakes for breakfast.
* She does not have breakfast at 8.30 am.
* Her favorite color is neither blue nor green.

Information derived from the lower gray row and the column – in other words, with reference to the true marker/tick (✓) in the Yellow/8.30 am box:

* The favorite color of the person who has breakfast at 8.30 am is yellow.
* This person has neither muesli nor yogurt for breakfast.
* This person is not Angela (because this person has breakfast at 8.30 am and Angela does not).

		Food					Time					Favorite color				
		Cakes	Ham & eggs	Muesli	Porridge	Yogurt	7.30 am	7.45 am	8.00 am	8.15 am	8.30 am	Blue	Green	Purple	Red	Yellow
Name	Angela	✓	×	×	×	×					×	×	×			
	Dennis	×														
	Maria	×														
	Mike	×														
	Pearl	×														
Favorite color	Blue										×					
	Green										×					
	Purple										×					
	Red										×					
	Yellow			×		×	×	×	×	×	✓					
Time	7.30 am															
	7.45 am															
	8.00 am															
	8.15 am															
	8.30 am															

Let's start with transpositions relating to the true marker/tick (✓) in the Angela/Cakes box. We can see that Angela – who has cakes for breakfast – does not eat at 8.30 am. Therefore, the cake eater does not have breakfast at 8.30 am.

� *Put a false marker/cross (✗) in the 8.30 am/Cakes box.*

We can also see that Angela's favorite color is not blue or green. Since we know that Angela is the cake eater, we can deduce that the cake eater's favorite color is not blue or green either.

↳ *Put false markers/crosses (✗) in the Blue/Cakes and Green/Cakes boxes.*

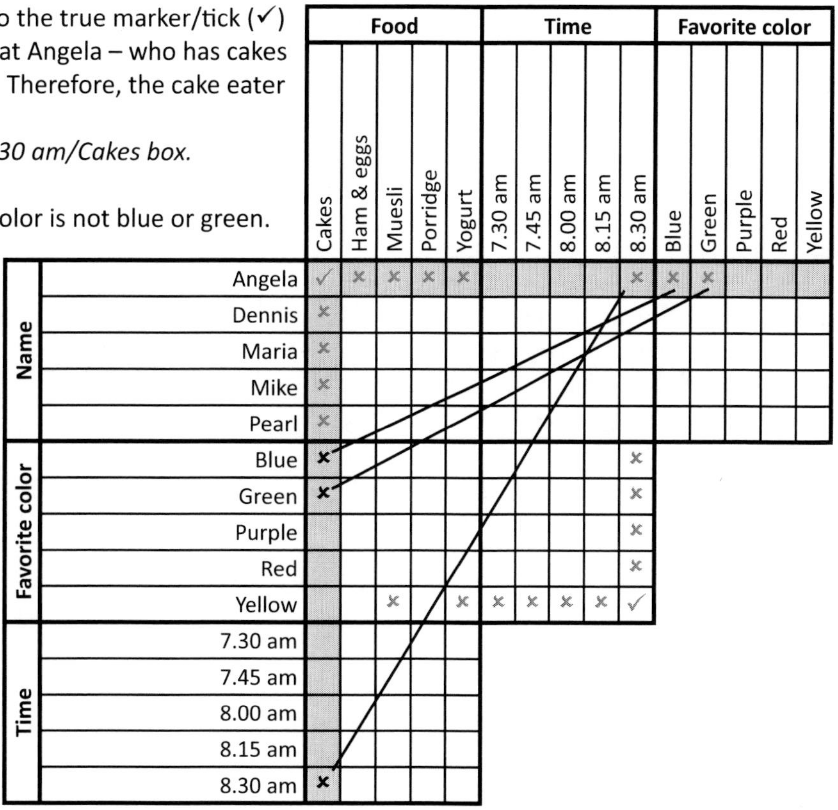

		Food					Time					Favorite color				
		Cakes	Ham & eggs	Muesli	Porridge	Yogurt	7.30 am	7.45 am	8.00 am	8.15 am	8.30 am	Blue	Green	Purple	Red	Yellow
Name	Angela	✓	✗	✗	✗	✗					✗	✗	✗			
	Dennis	✗														
	Maria	✗														
	Mike	✗														
	Pearl	✗														
Favorite color	Blue	✗									✗					
	Green	✗									✗					
	Purple										✗					
	Red										✗					
	Yellow		✗		✗		✗	✗	✗	✗	✓					
Time	7.30 am															
	7.45 am															
	8.00 am															
	8.15 am															
	8.30 am	✗														

Now that we've transposed the information relating to the true marker/tick (✓) in the Angela/Cakes box, we can move on to transposing information relating to the true marker/tick (✓) in the Yellow/8.30 am box. We can see that there is information relating to this box both on the corresponding row and column. Let's start with the row: This reveals to us that the person who has breakfast at 8.30 am and whose favorite color is yellow does not eat muesli or yogurt. In other words, there are false markers/crosses (✗) in the Yellow/Muesli and Yellow/Yogurt boxes. We can transpose these pieces of information into the botton row of the bottom section of the grid. In other words, the person who has breakfast at 8.30 am does not have muesli or yogurt.

↳ *Put false markers/crosses (✗) in the 8.30 am/Muesli and 8.30 am/Yogurt boxes.*

When we look at the column relating to the true marker/tick (✓) in the Yellow/8.30 am box, we can see that the person eating breakfast at 8.30 am is not Angela. In other words, there is a false marker/cross (✗) in the Angela/8.30 am box. Since the favorite color of the person who has breakfast at 8.30 am is yellow – as indicated by the true marker/tick (✓) in the Yellow/8.30 am box – we can deduce that Angela's favorite color cannot be yellow. We can traspose this piece of information into the last column of the section that is farthest right in the grid.

↳ *Put a false marker/cross (✗) in the Angela/Yellow box.*

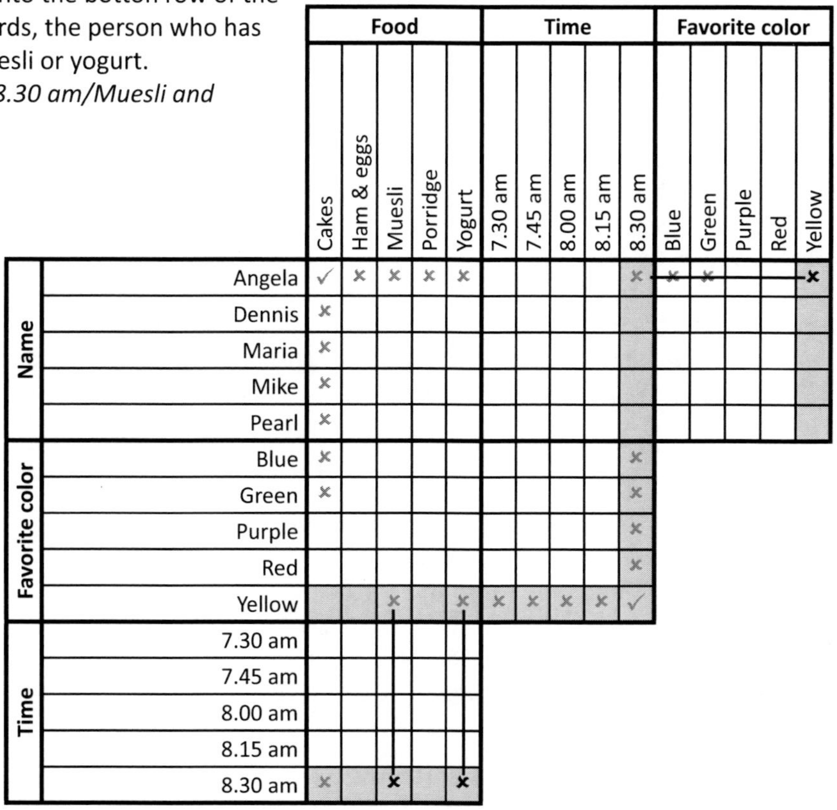

		Food					Time					Favorite color				
		Cakes	Ham & eggs	Muesli	Porridge	Yogurt	7.30 am	7.45 am	8.00 am	8.15 am	8.30 am	Blue	Green	Purple	Red	Yellow
Name	Angela	✓	✗	✗	✗	✗					✗	✗	✗			✗
	Dennis	✗														
	Maria	✗														
	Mike	✗														
	Pearl	✗														
Favorite color	Blue	✗									✗					
	Green	✗									✗					
	Purple										✗					
	Red										✗					
	Yellow		✗		✗		✗	✗	✗	✗	✓					
Time	7.30 am															
	7.45 am															
	8.00 am															
	8.15 am															
	8.30 am	✗		✗		✗										

Whenever we make transpositions, we add more information into the different parts of the grid. Therefore, we potentially discover new relationships between the different elements – and have more information that we can transpose. In our example so far, we first transposed information relating to the the true marker/tick (✓) in the Angela/Cakes box. After that we transposed information relating to the true marker/tick (✓) in the Yellow/8.30 am box. The latter potentially added more information with reference to the true marker/tick (✓) in the Angela/Cakes box. When we look at the grid, this is indeed the case: We can see that we added the piece of information that Angela's favorite color is not yellow. In other words, there is a false marker/cross (✗) in the Angela/Yellow box. Since Angela has cakes for breakfast, the cake eater's favorite color is not yellow either.
➻ *Put a false marker/cross (✗) in the Yellow/Cakes box.*

Now we have finished making all the possible transpositions. We would need further clues to continue solving the puzzle.

So far we have looked at transpositions where the focal point is the true marker/tick (✓). In certain situations it's also possible to use false markers/crosses (✗) as reference points. Let's look at some examples to clarify what these situations are and how we can make such transpositions.

This grid (of which only a part is shown) contains a number of false markers/crosses (✗).

When we look at the Name/Food category section in the grid, we can see that the gray rows that relate to Angela and Maria are identical. In other words, of Angela and Maria, one has cakes and the other yogurt for breakfast (but not necessarily in this order). This is to say to say that Dennis, Mike, and Pearl cannot have cakes or yogurt for breakfast.
➻ *Put false markers/crosses (✗) in the Dennis/Cakes, Dennis/Yogurt, Mike/Cakes, and Pearl/Yogurt boxes.* Since there are already false markers/crosses (✗) in the Mike/Yogurt and Pearl/Cakes boxes, we don't have to add them.

Next, we'll look at the Name/Time section. Let's say that we have a clue that states the following: **There's a 15-minute difference between Pearl and Dennis's breakfast times.**
We can see that Dennis's breakfast time is 8.00 am, 8.15 am, or 8.30 am, and Pearl's breakfast time is 7.30 am, 8.15 am, or 8.30 am. For the two breakfast times to be 15 minutes apart, Pearl's breakfast time cannot be 7.30 am.
➻ *Put a false marker/cross (✗) in the Pearl/7.30 am box.*

On the previous page we were working on this clue: ***There's a 15-minute difference between Pearl and Dennis's breakfast times.*** Now that we've narrowed down the options, we can see that Dennis's breakfast time options are 8.00 am, 8.15 am, and 8.30 am. Pearl's time options are 8.15 am and 8.30 am. It follows from this that the following combinations are possible:

If Dennis's breakfast time is either 8.00 am or 8.30 am, Pearl's breakfast time is 8.15 am.

If Dennis's breakfast time is 8.15 am, Pearl's breakfast time is 8.30 am.

In both cases 8.15 am is either Dennis or Pearl's time to have breakfast. Therefore, 8.15 am cannot be a time when Angela, Maria, or Mike have breakfast.

→ *Put false markers/crosses (✕) in the Angela/8.15 am, Maria/8.15 am, and Mike/8.15 am boxes.*

Name	Cakes	Ham & eggs	Muesli	Porridge	Yogurt	7.30 am	7.45 am	8.00 am	8.15 am	8.30 am	Blue	Green	Purple	Red	Yellow
Angela		✕	✕	✕					✕						
Dennis	✕	✕			✕	✕	✕								
Maria		✕	✕	✕					✕	✕					
Mike	✕			✕					✕						
Pearl	✕		✕		✕	✕	✕	✕							

Let's move on to more advanced transposition techniques. To illustrate them, we'll reveal the rest of the grid where more false markers/crosses (✕) have been added in the Favorite color/Food and Time/Food sections.

These new markers tell us that the favorite color of the people who have muesli and porridge for breakfast is not purple, and that the person who eats porridge does not have breakfast at 7.30 am, 8.15 am, or 8.30 am.

Whenever there are numerous false markers/crosses (✕) in the grid, we can look for a row or column within a section that inversely mirrors another row or column in another section. The idea is to try to find corresponding rows or columns which reveal that no match is possible between certain items. This works by using logic that states the following:

If X can only equal A, B, or C, and Y cannot be A, B, or C, then X cannot be Y.

We'll take an example of the Dennis row in the Name/Food section and the Purple row in the Favorite color/Food section. These are highlighted in gray. These rows show that Dennis has either muesli or porridge for breakfast, and that the person whose favorite color is purple does not have muesli or porridge for breakfast. We can, therefore, deduce that Dennis's favorite color cannot be purple.

→ *Put a false marker/cross (✕) in the Dennis/Purple box.*

	Cakes	Ham & eggs	Muesli	Porridge	Yogurt	7.30 am	7.45 am	8.00 am	8.15 am	8.30 am	Blue	Green	Purple	Red	Yellow
Angela		✕	✕	✕					✕						
Dennis	✕	✕			✕	✕	✕								
Maria		✕	✕	✕					✕	✕					
Mike	✕			✕					✕						
Pearl	✕		✕		✕	✕	✕	✕							
Blue															
Green															
Purple			✕	✕											
Red															
Yellow															
7.30 am				✕											
7.45 am															
8.00 am															
8.15 am				✕											
8.30 am				✕											

	Cakes	Ham & eggs	Muesli	Porridge	Yogurt	7.30 am	7.45 am	8.00 am	8.15 am	8.30 am	Blue	Green	Purple	Red	Yellow
Angela		✕	✕	✕					✕						
Dennis	✕	✕	✕	✕	✕	✕	✕						✕		
Maria		✕	✕	✕					✕	✕					
Mike	✕			✕					✕						
Pearl	✕		✕		✕	✕	✕	✕							
Blue															
Green															
Purple			✕	✕											
Red															
Yellow															
7.30 am				✕											
7.45 am															
8.00 am															
8.15 am				✕											
8.30 am				✕											

Using the logic of *"If X can only equal A, B, or C, and Y cannot be A, B, or C, then X cannot be Y."* is not limited to inverse mirror image lines. We can use the fact that we can see a lot of false markers/crosses (✗) in the grid as a prompt and, consequently, check if we can make any further deductions.

The next example can be found in the Pearl row in the Name/Time section and the Porridge column in the Time/Food section. Both are highlighted. The Pearl row tells us that she does not have breakfast at 7.30 am, 7.45 am, or 8.00 am. The Porridge column tells us that the person who eats porridge has breakfast either at 7.45 am or 8.00 am. This means that Pearl cannot have porridge for breakfast.
⇢ *Put a false marker/cross (✗) in the Pearl/Porridge box.*

		Cakes	Ham & eggs	Muesli	Porridge	Yogurt	7.30 am	7.45 am	8.00 am	8.15 am	8.30 am	Blue	Green	Purple	Red	Yellow
Name	Angela		✗	✗	✗					✗						
	Dennis	✗	✗			✗	✗	✗						✗		
	Maria		✗	✗	✗					✗	✗					
	Mike	✗				✗				✗						
	Pearl	✗		✗	**✗**	✗	✗	✗	✗							
Favorite color	Blue										
	Green										
	Purple			✗	✗						
	Red										
	Yellow										
Time	7.30 am				✗	
	7.45 am					
	8.00 am					
	8.15 am				✗	
	8.30 am				✗	

Now we can continue making further deductions. We can see that the only breakfast food option left for Pearl is ham and eggs.
⇢ *Put a true marker/tick (✓) in the Pearl/Ham & eggs box.*
It follows from this that no one else can have ham and eggs for breakfast. Since there are already some false markers/crosses (✗) in place, there is only one more to add.
⇢ *Put a false marker/cross (✗) in the Mike/Ham & eggs box.*

Now that we have added a true marker/tick (✓) in the grid, we need to see if we can transpose any further information. And indeed we can: We can see that Pearl does not have breakfast at 7.30 am, 7.45 am, or 8.00 am. Since Pearl has ham and eggs for breakfast, the ham-and-eggs eater cannot have breakfast at 7.30 am, 7.45 am, or 8.00 am either.
⇢ *Put false markers/crosses (✗) in the 7.30 am/ Ham & eggs, 7.45 am/Ham & eggs, and 8.00 am/ Ham & eggs boxes.*

		Cakes	Ham & eggs	Muesli	Porridge	Yogurt	7.30 am	7.45 am	8.00 am	8.15 am	8.30 am	Blue	Green	Purple	Red	Yellow
Name	Angela		✗	✗	✗					✗						
	Dennis	✗	✗			✗	✗	✗						✗		
	Maria		✗	✗	✗					✗	✗					
	Mike	✗	**✗**			✗				✗				**✗**		
	Pearl	✗	✓	✗	✗	✗	✗	✗	✗							
Favorite color	Blue										
	Green										
	Purple			✗	✗						
	Red										
	Yellow										
Time	7.30 am		**✗**		✗	
	7.45 am		**✗**			
	8.00 am		**✗**			
	8.15 am				✗	
	8.30 am				✗	

Finally, we can see that Mike's row in the Name/Food section is now identical to that of Dennis's row. On the previous page we deduced that Dennis's favorite color is not purple because his choice of breakfast is either muesli or porridge and the person whose favorite color is purple does not eat muesli or porridge for breakfast. Since we now know that Mike has either muesli or porridge for breakfast, his favorite color cannot be purple.
⇢ *Put a false marker/cross (✗) in the Mike/Purple box.*

Connecting information in two or more clues

Many of the puzzles contain clues that are linked in a way that when they are read individually, they may not mean very much, but when they're read together, there is information that can be extracted. For example, if one clue states that a woman who wears red clothes likes cakes and another clue states that the name of the woman who wears red clothes is Angela, we can deduce that Angela likes cakes.

Male and female names and pronouns

This book contains a lot of names that are not easily identifiable as male or female. If the gender is relevant in a puzzle, the clues will give enough information so it's possible to deduce the gender of the names.

Watch out for male and female pronouns (or other gender descriptions) in the clues. These can be subtle and may be easy to miss. However, knowing a person's gender helps you extract information accordingly.

Alternative expressions

Sometimes information is expressed in a way that the wording in the clues and the grid is not identical. For example, if someone does not say anything in the clue, the corresponding option in the grid could be that the person is silent.

Also, when family relations are mentioned, pay particular attention to the point of reference that's being used: the grandmother's husband could refer to the grandchild's grandfather while the grandchild's mother could be the grandmother's daughter or daughter-in-law.

Math-based clues

Some clues require you to do some math. You may need to calculate different combinations of numbers. Feel free to jot down your calculations in the margins of the book or on a separate sheet of paper. If you prefer to use a calculator, by all means do so.

We have now looked at a number of ways in which information can be extracted from the clues and transposed within the grid. The examples and tips are not an exhaustive list of all the possible ways, but they give some ideas to get you started. I hope you have fun discovering further methods to solve logic grid puzzles.

Enjoy the puzzles!

1. Treemendous Decorations

It was the first day of December and Santa Claus was keen to spread Christmas cheer among his household. He asked five of his interior designer elves to find the prettiest Christmas trees in the forest behind his workshop, bring them in, and decorate them in a way that would bring smiles to everyone's faces and the spirit of Christmas into their hearts. Using the clues, can you work out how tall each elf's chosen Christmas tree was, where they placed the trees, and what their decorative themes were?

1. When Santa entered the library at the end of the day, he was surprised to see a Christmas tree with plump, green frogs made out of felt hanging between green and yellow fairy lights. Santa thought that perhaps the elf whose decision it was to choose the theme of Hoppy Holidays had not quite understood the task.

2. The elf whose Christmas tree was more than twenty centimeters shorter than Ivy League's tree had lots of tangled tinsel on its branches. This tree was not placed in the gourmet kitchen – which was just as well because Santa knew that Mrs Claus would not have been pleased to look at the messy display every time she went to inspect what the kitchen elves were doing.

3. As Mrs Claus walked into the post office, she noticed that the otherwise perfectly baked, loveheart-shaped gingerbread cookies that decorated the Christmas tree there had something odd about them: there was a bite-sized piece missing from each of them! The elf, whose tree was fifty-five centimeters shorter than Holly Wood's tree, defended her actions as she was wiping crumbs from around her mouth, "My theme is called Love at First Bite so I had to take a bite out of every cookie. It's got nothing to do with my perchant for gingerbread cookies…"

4. There was a forty-five-centimeter height difference between Douglas Fir's tree and the tree whose theme was Glow-Ho-Ho. Neither tree was displayed in the Excellent Elf School.

5. Santa was most impressed by the tree whose theme was the Elphabet. The elf responsible for this creation enjoyed glass-blowing and she had blown a glass alphabet with decorative elves hanging from them in funny poses. These would surely encourage the youngest elflings-in-training to learn their alphabet when they attended the Excellent Elf School.

6. Of Juniper Berry and Rosemary Pine, one's theme was Tinsel in a Tangle and the other's tree was the shortest.

7. The tree that was displayed in Santa's workshop was decorated by an elf whose last name had one more letter than the last name of the elf whose tree was the tallest.

		Height					Theme					Place				
		2 m 25 cm	2 m 35 cm	2 m 60 cm	2 m 80 cm	3 m 5 cm	Elphabet	Glow-Ho-Ho	Hoppy Holidays	Love at First Bite	Tinsel in a Tangle	Excellent Elf School	Gourmet kitchen	Library	Post office	Workshop
Elf	Douglas Fir															
	Holly Wood															
	Ivy League															
	Juniper Berry															
	Rosemary Pine															
Place	Excellent Elf School															
	Gourmet kitchen															
	Library															
	Post office															
	Workshop															
Theme	Elphabet															
	Glow-Ho-Ho															
	Hoppy Holidays															
	Love at First Bite															
	Tinsel in a Tangle															

Elf	Height	Theme	Place
Douglas Fir			
Holly Wood			
Ivy League			
Juniper Berry			
Rosemary Pine			

2. Rude-olph Awakenings

Tinsel Cheeks, the spokesreindeer of Santa's reindeer herd, submitted to the Reindeer Affairs Committee a request that had been widely discussed among all the reindeer in the past few weeks. Everyone was fed up with being woken up abruptly in the mornings, and therefore, the herd had come up with an alternative idea: Their days in the run up to Christmas should start gently with some music being played in the background as they slowly opened their eyes and got up from their cozy beds. Afterwards, they should ease into the day by watching an uplifting movie. Although at first the Committee was somewhat surprised to receive such a request, they agreed to give it a try for the rest of the week. Using the clues, can you figure out the suggested rota for the rest of the week – in other words, when the different elves will be on wake-up duty, which musician's songs will be played, and which movies will be watched on which days?

1. Tinsel Cheeks is looking forward to being woken up to Rudolph's favorite pop star Beyond Sleigh and her songs *All the Jingle Ladies* and *If I Were a Toy* two days earlier than when the movie *Pear Exports* will be watched.

2. Perry Pheral will not be the first elf on wake-up duty this week. He will be further disappointed that he won't be playing two of his favorite songs, namely, Elfric Clapton's *Cheers in Heaven* and *Wonderful Moonlight*.

3. *The Molar Express* and *The Nightwear before Christmas* will not be watched on consecutive days. If it's *The Molar Express* that's watched earlier in the week, the elf on wake-up duty that day will be Perry Pheral. If, instead, *The Nightwear before Christmas* is watched earlier in the week, Amy Pinehouse's *Gallery* and *Love Is an Oozing Flame* will be the wake-up songs on Saturday.

4. Perry Scope and Perri Stalsis will be on duty earlier in the week than when Spruce Springsteen's songs *Born to Stun* and *Horn in the USA* will be waking up the reindeer.

5. *Bake It Off* by Taylor Drift will be the wake-up song on the morning when Perri Patetic is on duty. This will not be the same day that *Glove Actually* or *The Dough Man* will be watched.

6. Perrie Odical can't wait to be on duty as she hasn't seen *Pear Exports* before and wants to join the reindeer in Santa's outdoor cinema after waking them up. The day when she'll be on duty is one day after when *The Nightwear before Christmas* is watched and two days before Perri Patetic will be on duty.

7. It is one of the elves with the first name Perry who will be playing Rudolph's favorite pop star's songs. This is not the elf who'll be showing the movie *Glove Actually*.

	Movie					Musician					Day				
	Glove Actually	Pear Exports	The Dough Man	The Molar Express	The Nightwear before Christmas	Amy Pinehouse	Beyond Sleigh	Elfric Clapton	Spruce Springsteen	Taylor Drift	Wednesday	Thursday	Friday	Saturday	Sunday
Elf Perrie Odical															
Perri Patetic															
Perri Stalsis															
Perry Pheral															
Perry Scope															
Day Wednesday															
Thursday															
Friday															
Saturday															
Sunday															
Musician Amy Pinehouse															
Beyond Sleigh															
Elfric Clapton															
Spruce Springsteen															
Taylor Drift															

Elf	Movie	Musician	Day
Perrie Odical			
Perri Patetic			
Perri Stalsis			
Perry Pheral			
Perry Scope			

3. Rolling Out the Dough-Ho-Ho

The annual Gingerbread House Party was Mrs Claus' way to get the festive season started. Each year she invited five junior kitchen elves who had aspirations of becoming grand cookie artists to make some magnificent gingerbread houses. After toiling in the gourmet kitchen for two full days, these elves were about to reveal their masterpieces, and get the party started. Cam Era, the Head Photographer Elf, was ready to immortalize them and their creations. Using the clues and the sketch of Cam Era's photograph, can you work out where each elf was in the photo, what the different accidents were that happened to the elves while they were making their splendid gingerbread houses, and what their quick fixes were to rectify their respective adversities?

1. *A Claus Shave* was meant to depict Santa having a shave inside a wooden cabin. However, something unforeseen happened and its creator didn't have time to fix the damage and, hence, resorted to hiding behind a pile of presents in Cam Era's photo.

2. Hazel Nut used a grater to sand the edges of the walls before starting to assemble her gingerbread house. Unfortunately, she was a little heavy-handed and ended up shaving off a little too much from some wall pieces while others actually broke. It took an awful lot of caramelized sugar to repair the walls. The end result was not pretty, with all the walls wonky one way or another. And what's more, she hadn't even started to assemble her gingerbread house yet! She was going to have to be very inventive in order to make her gingerbread house stand.

3. The elf who left her gingerbread house pieces in the oven for too long and burnt them all was standing in Cam Era's photo directly between Candy Cane and the elf whose creation's roof fell down.

4. The gingerbread house that collapsed completely should have been name *Ruined Cottage in a Forest* – provided two fir trees standing on either side of the rubble that used to be a house was considered a forest. The elf who created this masterpiece tried to cover up the accident by placing a plastic dinosaur behind the collapsed house, to indicate that the scene of devastation was entirely planned.

5. *Someone's Barking up the Wrong Christmas Tree* was supposed to have been a treehouse. If you really looked at it, you could sort of imagine it, thanks to copious amounts of super glue that had been used in its repair works.

6. It was either the gingerbread castle or the igloo-shaped gingerbread house called *Boldly Go Where No Snowman Has Ever Gone Before* that was propped up with some cardboard scaffolding.

7. It was not Cherry Pie who created *What's the Poinsettia?* The place number of the former was one lower than the place number of the latter.

8. Justin Thyme was the only male elf participating in the gingerbread house making this year. He attempted to make a treehouse.

9. The elf whose marzipan and chocolate-drop decorations were licked off by a reindeer was furious at the elf who had opened the kitchen door in order to let the smoke out when she had burnt her gingerbread house pieces. Didn't she realize that it was an open invitation to all the reindeer to just wander in? Neither of these elves posed in the middle of the photo.

10. The elf who had resorted to turning her house from a 3D construction into a 2D gingerbread picture occupied a place in the photo was three numbers higher than the place of the elf who had used cardboard scaffolding to prop up her house.

11. The decorations of the gingerbread treehouse weren't particularly appealing to the reindeer, nor was the creation right next to it in Cam Era's picture.

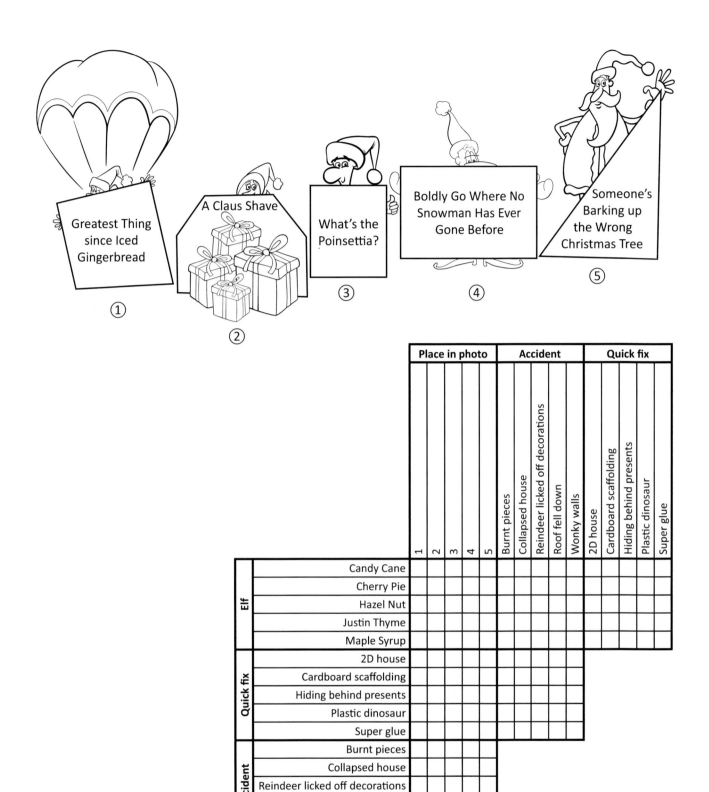

1. Greatest Thing since Iced Gingerbread
2. A Claus Shave
3. What's the Poinsettia?
4. Boldly Go Where No Snowman Has Ever Gone Before
5. Someone's Barking up the Wrong Christmas Tree

		Place in photo					Accident					Quick fix				
		1	2	3	4	5	Burnt pieces	Collapsed house	Reindeer licked off decorations	Roof fell down	Wonky walls	2D house	Cardboard scaffolding	Hiding behind presents	Plastic dinosaur	Super glue
Elf	Candy Cane															
	Cherry Pie															
	Hazel Nut															
	Justin Thyme															
	Maple Syrup															
Quick fix	2D house															
	Cardboard scaffolding															
	Hiding behind presents															
	Plastic dinosaur															
	Super glue															
Accident	Burnt pieces															
	Collapsed house															
	Reindeer licked off decorations															
	Roof fell down															
	Wonky walls															

Elf	Place in photo	Accident	Quick fix
Candy Cane			
Cherry Pie			
Hazel Nut			
Justin Thyme			
Maple Syrup			

4. Sweater You Like It or Not, I'm Wearing It!

The annual Gingerbread House Party was well under way. Prancers' Enhancers, the festive house band, was playing funky festive tunes, fairy lights were twinkling, and the elves were dancing the night away. Among the dancing elves, the members of the Excellent Elf School's five knitting clubs were proudly showing off what they had been working on for months: their lovingly-knitted Christmas sweaters. Using the clues, can you figure out how many members each knitting club had, what each club's Christmas sweater design was, and what kind of unusual detail was incorporated into each of the designs?

1. The different knitting clubs couldn't agree whether their creations should be called sweaters or jumpers. Three clubs called them jumpers and two clubs called them sweaters. Of the clubs that called their knitted garments jumpers, it was the one that was second in alphabetical order that had designed *Sleigh-ing It*. This club had one more member than the club whose idea it was to have an artificial Christmas tree pop up behind the wearer's head whenever someone twisted a pom-pom attached to the pattern featuring a snowy chimney.

2. The members of Pins & Needles were proud of their sweater design that depicted a snowy evergreen forest where, oddly, each tree wore detachable Christmas goggles.

3. *All Good Things Come in Trees* incorporated a button feature on the sleeve that sounded a warning saying, "Step away from the cookie jar!" The knitting club that had come up with this ingenious sweater had two fewer members than Black Sheep.

4. The club whose jumpers incorporated kangaroo pouches (filled with chocolate truffles) had one fewer member than the club that created *Too Cool for Yule*.

5. The combined number of members in the knitting clubs Knit Me Baby One More Time and In Stitches was twelve. The one that had more members called their festive garments jumpers and the other called them sweaters.

6. The number of Woolverines' members was one fewer than the club whose jumper, quite bizarrely, had a feature where a pair of short, narrow skis would slide down from the sleeves at a pull of a ribbon.

7. The sweater *Time to Spruce Things Up!* was created by a club that had one more member than In Stitches and two fewer members than Woolverines.

Knitting club	Design					How many					Unusual detail				
	All Good Things Come in Trees	Hairy Christmas	Sleigh-ing It	Time to Spruce Things Up!	Too Cool for Yule	4	5	6	7	8	Detachable Christmas goggles	Kangaroo pouch	Pop-up Christmas tree	Skis in sleeves	Warning button
Black Sheep															
In Stitches															
Knit Me Baby One More Time															
Pins & Needles															
Woolverines															
Detachable Christmas goggles															
Kangaroo pouch															
Pop-up Christmas tree															
Skis in sleeves															
Warning button															
4															
5															
6															
7															
8															

Knitting club	Design	How many	Unusual detail
Black Sheep			
In Stitches			
Knit Me Baby One More Time			
Pins & Needles			
Woolverines			

5. There's Snow Place Like Home

Angie Near, the Head Elf of the Engineering Unit, looked out of the window and noticed that not only was it snowing, but that the snow's consistency seemed perfect for building snow castles. Although she was supposed to be concentrating on improving the aerodynamic features of Santa's sleigh, she suggested that the rest of the engineering team should meet outdoors after lunch and have a snow castle construction competition. She proposed that the teams should build aesthetically pleasing castles and that they should also make them their homes until Christmas to prove that their engineering was sound. Using the clues and the diagram, can you figure out which elf was the captain of which team, where their snow castles were located, and what problem each team experienced?

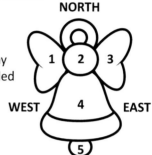

1. Angie Near went outside and drew a Christmas bell on the snow with some red spray paint she had found in Santa's workshop. She demarcated five areas within the bell and allocated these areas to the different teams. The team in Area 5 (which did not touch any other teams' areas) blamed her for giving them so little space that their snow castle ended up being so small that there was not enough space for everyone in the team to fit into it. Angie Near didn't have any sympathy, though, as nowhere in the rules did it say that the snow castles had to be one-storey constructions.

2. Snow Lily's team's area was farther north from the area where Not So Great Expectations built their castle. Her team's area did not touch the Parumpapapums's area.

3. Angie Near couldn't believe that the team whose area touched the west side of North Pole's team's area and the northwest side of Crystal Clear's team's area hadn't hosed their castle walls with water in order to turn them into ice. No wonder one of the walls partly collapsed and a huge hole appeared. Frosty Fern's cousin's team, in contrast, was too hasty with hosing water all over their castle: by the time they realized their castle was missing a door, all the walls were solid ice and there was no getting into the castle.

4. Rooftop Rebels' area was not adjacent to Fa La La Family's area. The captain of the former team was the uncle of Crystal Clear and the proud dad of triplets: Breeze Block; the captain of the team whose castle was too small; and the captain of Snow Angels (whose area number was higher than her dad's).

5. Just as Angie Near announced that all the teams were hopeless, Santa appeared. He was astonished to see the odd-shaped castle east of the one that had a collapsed roof. He retrieved his spray paint can and started walking back to his workshop. If you looked very carefully, you could see that he was trying to suppress an amused smile.

		Area					Team					Problem				
		1	2	3	4	5	Fa La La Family	Not So Great Expectations	Rooftop Rebels	Snow Angels	The Parumpapapums	Hole in the wall	No door	Odd shape	Roof collapsed	Too small
Captain	Breeze Block															
	Crystal Clear															
	Frosty Fern															
	North Pole															
	Snow Lily															
Problem	Hole in the wall															
	No door															
	Odd shape															
	Roof collapsed															
	Too small															
Team	Fa La La Family															
	Not So Great Expectations															
	Rooftop Rebels															
	Snow Angels															
	The Parumpapapums															

Captain	Area	Team	Problem
Breeze Block			
Crystal Clear			
Frosty Fern			
North Pole			
Snow Lily			

6. Elf Portrait

An increasing number of elves had started growing beards, and Cam Era was one of them. Being the Head Photographer Elf (or Santa's Head Snapper as the rest of the elves liked to call him), he thought it would be fun to take an elf portrait. His five best friends were delighted about the idea and thought it would make a lovely Christmas card that they could give to Santa. Using the clues and the picture, can you figure out where each of Cam Era's best friends were in the elf portrait, why they had chosen to grow facial hair, and how long it took them each morning to comb their beards?

1. Elfred Einstein hadn't planned on growing a beard, but because initially he had forgotten to shave for a few weeks, he decided to forget the whole thing and just let his beard do whatever it wanted.

2. The elf who frequently lost his gloves and, hence, used his beard as a muff to keep his hands warm in the wintry weather, spent two minutes longer combing his beard than the elf who was in Place 4 in the photo.

3. The combined beard combing time of the elves in Places 1 and 3 was less than how long Elfis Presley spent making sure his facial hair looked stunning. Elfis was known for his velvety singing voice and his unique way of making his beard move when he was performing. The other elves still remembered his outrageously fabulous performance of *Yule Suede Shoes* at last year's Christmas concert.

4. Three of Cam Era's best friends wanted to be clearly visible in the portrait. They positioned themselves in front of the elf crowd and were near the bottom edge of the photo. All of them were accomplished singers (unlike Cam Era's other two friends who were tone-deaf). They also occupied lead vocalist positions in their respective choirs. None of them were as quick to comb their beards in the mornings as the elf in Place 1.

5. The elf who had grown a beard in order to keep his face warm had the shortest beard-combing time.

6. Of the three lead vocalist elves, one had grown a beard because he had lost a dare and another was called Elfon John. The third one spent one minute less time grooming in the mornings than the elf in Place 2.

7. Elfon John was hoping that his choir would sing *Yule Eyes* in the forthcoming Christmas concert. This song would allow him to show off his singing voice – as well as his magnificent beard which took three minutes longer to comb than the beard of the elf in Place 2.

8. Elf Sheeran was one of the two elves who stood next to each other in front of the elf crowd. His favorite song was *Shape of Yule* and he repeatedly sang it whenever he was showering.

		Place in photo					Why beard					Combing time				
		1	2	3	4	5	Forgot to shave	Keeps face warm	Keeps hands warm	Looks Christmassy	Lost a dare	1 min	3 mins	4 mins	5 mins	7 mins
Elf	Billy Elfiot															
	Elfis Presley															
	Elfon John															
	Elfred Einstein															
	Elf Sheeran															
Combing time	1 min															
	3 mins															
	4 mins															
	5 mins															
	7 mins															
Why beard	Forgot to shave															
	Keeps face warm															
	Keeps hands warm															
	Looks Christmassy															
	Lost a dare															

Elf	Place in photo	Why beard	Combing time
Billy Elfiot			
Elfis Presley			
Elfon John			
Elfred Einstein			
Elf Sheeran			

7. Behind Claused Doors

Yule Befine, Santa's Chief Personal Assistant, was busy making preparations for Santa's grand tour around the world. Last year her trusted team of elves had retired and now she had a new cohort of elves helping her. This morning she had asked them to find all the relevant maps in Santa's library and put them into the Very Important Maps satchel so that they would be ready for Santa when he needed them. Using the clues and the picture, can you work out which elf found which map in the library, on which shelf, and next to which book?

1. The five assistant elves spent the morning in Santa's library, searching for relevant maps. It seemed like there was no one place where the maps were stored, which puzzled them. Hence, they started taking books off the shelves, and, surprisingly, found a number of maps stashed between them. Britney Steers found a map on a higher shelf than Elf Dorado.

2. The elf who came across a piece of paper with the heading *Inclusion Map*, followed by scribbles resembling mathematical equations, didn't quite know what to make of it. Since the heading said it was a map, he took it and placed it in the Very Important Maps satchel. This map was not found next to *The Jingle Bell Jar* (which was on a higher shelf).

3. A mind map that had Mrs Claus' unmistakeable handwriting on it and contained ideas for novel Christmas tea flavors was found two shelves lower than where *Noel Country for Old Men* was. The higher of these shelves had black folders on it.

4. The elf who found the last map took it out from the middle shelf.

5. Joy Ride and Max Speed were quite short and couldn't reach the highest shelf. Therefore, they focused on finding maps on lower shelves. Neither came across the document titled *Heat Map* (even though it would have been within their reach). If they had, they would have known that this kind of data visualization technique would not be very helpful for Santa on his trip to deliver presents to all the kids around the world.

6. *Fifty Shades of Sleigh* was Rudolph's favorite book, which is why he had placed the genetic map of reindeer next to it when he had received it from a scientific research team. The elf who found it had the letter E in her last name.

7. Harry Caine knew that fate mapping was used to study the embryonic origin of adult tissues and structures. Therefore, even though he saw it on a shelf right above *Alice in Winter Wonderland*, he left it there and continued searching for other kinds of maps.

8. *Frankinscence and Sensibility* was not on the shelf where Max Speed spotted a map. The shelf where he found a map had black folders on it.

9. Rudolph's favorite book was on a higher shelf than the heat map, which, in turn, was higher than the inclusion map. None of these were on a shelf where Joy Ride found a map that she put into the Very Important Maps satchel.

10. *Alice in Winter Wonderland* was on a shelf that had black folders on it.

11. Elf Dorado found the last map and put it into the Very Important Maps satchel. As he handed the satchel to Yule Befine, he said, "We've finished the task. Here are all the maps, and they're organized in alphabetical order. That's a job you won't have to worry about now!"

		Fate map	Genetic map	Heat map	Inclusion map	Mind map	1	2	3	4	5	Alice in Winter Wonderland	Fifty Shades of Sleigh	Frankincense and Sensibility	Noel Country for Old Men	The Jingle Bell Jar
Elf	Britney Steers															
	Elf Dorado															
	Harry Caine															
	Joy Ride															
	Max Speed															
Next to book	Alice in Winter Wonderland															
	Fifty Shades of Sleigh															
	Frankincense and Sensibility															
	Noel Country for Old Men															
	The Jingle Bell Jar															
Shelf	1															
	2															
	3															
	4															
	5															

Elf	Map	Shelf	Next to book
Britney Steers			
Elf Dorado			
Harry Caine			
Joy Ride			
Max Speed			

8. Candy Canes in Mint Condition

Five apprentice pastry chef elves were trusted to make this year's candy canes for the whole of the Claus household. They were eager to impress Santa and Mrs Claus and duly proceeded to not only make candy canes, but to also turn them into elaborate art displays. Mrs Claus suggested they use *The Twelve Days of Christmas* as their inspiration. Unfortunately, the elves misheard what she had said and their displays ended up looking a little different from what had been intended. Using the clues, can you work out which elf created which display, what their candy cane flavors were, and how many canes were in each display?

1. Angel Cake had intertwined festive red and green colors into her candy canes even though neither color really depicted her chosen flavors – unless the tenuous link to green pumpkin stems was considered to be part of her decision-making process.

2. The combined number of candy canes whose flavors included cinnamon was fewer than 130.

3. Santa was rather puzzled when he saw a display where pairs of candy canes were neatly lined up one pair after another. He was told that these candy cane pairs were the runners of sleighs, which is why the artwork was called *Twelve Sleighs of Christmas*. Except there were more sleighs in the display than that: thirty-four to be precise.

4. Ginger Bread's artwork consisted of over ten more candy canes than *Twelve Sprays of Christmas*. The latter's creator was not keen on any pie flavors and avoided them at all costs.

5. The elf whose abstract display showed yellow-and-white canes organized into twelve roads leading to Christmas intended to use seventy canes, but since some had broken (and were promptly eaten), each of the 'Twelve Ways' was a little shorter than planned.

6. Of *Twelve Plays of Christmas* and Devon Cream's creation, one had vanilla in it and the other had three fewer canes than the display made of coffee-and-caramel canes.

7. Basil Oil burned his fingers as he was twisting his canes. His artwork had more canes than either of the displays of his fellow elves whose first names had the letter A in them.

8. Although Santa and Mrs Claus were not prepared to promote any of the apprentice pastry chef elves just yet, they were delighted that all the candy canes tasted delicious (even if the displays themselves were somewhat strange). The two couldn't agree whether it was Ginger Bread's canes or the canes in *Twelve Plays of Christmas* that were the best tasting.

	Flavor					Display title					How many				
	Apple pie & cinnamon	Blueberry pie & vanilla	Chocolate & mint	Coffee & caramel	Pumpkin pie & cinnamon	Twelve Plays of Christmas	Twelve Sleighs of Christmas	Twelve Sprays of Christmas	Twelve Trays of Christmas	Twelve Ways of Christmas	60	63	68	70	75
Elf Angel Cake															
Basil Oil																
Cedar Apple																
Devon Cream																
Ginger Bread																
How many 60											
63											
68											
70											
75											
Display title Twelve Plays of Christmas						
Twelve Sleighs of Christmas						
Twelve Sprays of Christmas						
Twelve Trays of Christmas						
Twelve Ways of Christmas						

Elf	Flavor	Display title	How many
Angel Cake			
Basil Oil			
Cedar Apple			
Devon Cream			
Ginger Bread			

9. Holding on for Deer Life

Rudolph was concerned that his reindeer had been overindulging over the past eleven months and might no longer be on top form. He suggested to the Head Elf of the Reindeer Affairs Committee that they organize a race to find out if any of them needed a last-minute bootcamp to be ready for their Christmas duties. Using the clues, can you figure out which elf was paired with which reindeer, how each pair ranked in the race, and what slowed them down?

1. Rudolph's reindeer race had the following rules: An elf would be randomly matched with a reindeer. The elves would be on skis and harnessed reindeer would pull them around the frozen lake. Everyone would start the race at the same time and whoever passed the finish line first would be the winner. The reindeer who came fourth and fifth would be taking part in Rudoph's bootcamp until Christmas Eve.

2. Reinald Deere blamed his elf in a red ski suit for ending up at Rudolph's bootcamp instead of being fed candy canes. He was sure that he could have won the race. He had even knocked another elf at the beginning of the race to try to make sure that this favorite pairing would not win, but unfortunately, they did.

3. Owot Fun came one place higher than the elf whose steering left much to be desired, but one place lower than Reinbert Deerling. The only female reindeer came three places lower than Reinhard Deerow.

4. Jingle Belle's boyfriend had trouble preparing his skis for the race. As a consequence, they were too slippery and his finish time was four minutes twenty-five seconds, which was fifteen seconds more than his girlfriend's.

5. Reinhild Deersley's racing time was five minutes twenty-two seconds. Although not last, she would've been faster if she'd been paired with an elf whose attention was not on admiring Ryde Ansing's red and Wunorse Openslae's green ski suits.

6. Reinbald Deerey thought his elf looked funny in his yellow ski suit – but not as funny as the elf who resembled a balloon about to float into the sky. Such a ski suit surely couldn't be very aerodynamic.

7. The fastest race time was four minutes ten seconds. Considering the world record was just under two minutes thirty seconds, Rudolph was not terribly impressed. However, as he was analyzing the race afterwards, he came to the conclusion that perhaps his reindeer were not to blame. Perhaps it was the elves who needed more training. For instance, the two male elves in yellow ski suits could have easily had better steering and avoided falling over if they had practiced more.

		Reindeer					Ranking					Slowed down by				
		Reinald Deere	Reinbald Deerey	Reinbert Deerling	Reinhard Deerow	Reinhild Deersley	1st	2nd	3rd	4th	5th	Falling over	Knocked by another reindeer	Non-aerodynamic ski suit	Poor steering	Too slippery skis
Elf	Dashin Throothesnoe															
	Jingle Belle															
	Owot Fun															
	Ryde Ansing															
	Wunorse Openslae															
Slowed down by	Falling over															
	Knocked by another reindeer															
	Non-aerodynamic ski suit															
	Poor steering															
	Too slippery skis															
Ranking	1st															
	2nd															
	3rd															
	4th															
	5th															

Elf	Reindeer	Ranking	Slowed down by
Dashin Throothesnoe			
Jingle Belle			
Owot Fun			
Ryde Ansing			
Wunorse Openslae			

10. Oh Christmas Tea, Oh Christmas Tea

Mrs Claus had spent all year developing new, tantalizing tea recipes. She was about to reveal her secret creations at a grand tea party when she discovered that some elves had broken into her private kitchen and mixed up all the ingredients in her jars. Using the clues, can you work out each new tea blend's original spice and its jar number, as well as what the new spices put into these jars were?

1. When Mrs Claus looked at her jar collection more closely, she noticed that not only had all the ingredients been mixed up, but all the numbered labels had been turned upside down. Her heart sank even further when she realized that most jars were no longer where she had placed them, but the jars with numbers that made sense even in their upside-down orientation had in many cases been moved. Originally, she had the jars numbered 1–25 on the first shelf (which was the top shelf), the jars numbered 26–50 on the second shelf, the jars numbered 51–75 on the third shelf, and the jars numbered 76–100 on the fourth shelf (which was the lowest shelf). The shelves still had correctly numbered jars on them – clearly in an attempt to fool Mrs Claus – but she was not going to fall for this kind of trick and promptly started to turn the labels the right way up and to reorganize her jars on the shelves. Unfortunately, sorting out the jars' contents wasn't as straightforward.

2. Of the five jars whose contents Mrs Claus had planned to use to make her special tea blends, three were found on the lowest shelf after the elves' break-in and two on the top shelf. One of the former should have containted cinnamon while one of the latter should have contained the spice for Mulled Pine.

3. The jar number that remained the same even when turned upside down had not contained nutmeg (which Mrs Claus planned to use for Nutmeg Nog). Instead, this jar should have contained a spice that had one more M letter in it than the original spice in a jar that sat before and after the elves' naughty visit on the bottom shelf.

4. The jars now containing cayenne pepper and paprika were originally on the first and third shelves (but not necessarily in this order).

5. The elves had tried to contaminate Mrs Claus' favorite tea blend with mustard. This jar's upside-down number was five numbers lower than the upside-down number of the spice for Most Wonderful Lime.

6. The elves avoided replacing original jar contents with spices whose names started with the same letter.

7. The jar number for Naughty or Spice's spice was higher before and after the elves' break-in than the original and upside-down numbers of the jar where cardamom should have been. However, this jar wasn't the one whose number remained the same even when its label was turned upside down.

8. Cayenne pepper and nutmeg were in two jars whose numbers were transposed when the labels were turned upside down.

	Original jar no.					Original spice					New spice				
	16	61	91	96	98	Cardamom	Cinnamon	Cloves	Ginger	Nutmeg	Cayenne pepper	Cumin	Garam masala	Mustard	Paprika
Tea blend Berry and Bright															
Most Wonderful Lime															
Mulled Pine															
Nutmeg Nog															
Naughty or Spice															
New spice Cayenne pepper															
Cumin															
Garam masala															
Mustard															
Paprika															
Original spice Cardamom															
Cinnamon															
Cloves															
Ginger															
Nutmeg															

Tea blend	Original jar no.	Original spice	New spice
Berry and Bright			
Most Wonderful Lime			
Mulled Pine			
Nutmeg Nog			
Naughty or Spice			

11. Truly, Medley, Deeply

Santa's annual Christmas concert is always full of festive spirit, with the music hall's walls adorned with decorative evergreen wreaths, mistletoe, and an abundance of fairy lights. This year five elf choirs were asked to prepare Christmas medleys. Unfortunately, a number of elves in each group reported having fallen ill. It was rather peculiar that each choir was affected by an ailment specific to that group. Using the clues, can you figure out what the first song in each choir's medley was, which mysterious illness affected each choir's members, and how many healthy elves in each choir actually turned up to perform?

1. Each choir was supposed to consist of twenty-three singers, but none had their full membership present. Lil' Drummer Dudettes, an all-female choir, had four more singers performing on the night than the only all-male choir, but fewer performers than the choir whose first song in their medley was *Jingle Bell Sock*.

2. If it hadn't been for Mrs Claus finding out that it was the choir missing three members who'd broken into her private kitchen and from whom she had subsequently banned all treats until further notice, this group might very well have been affected by mince pie malady or figgy pudding feebleness.

3. *Santa Claus Is Humming, "Calm Down."* was the first song in the medley that was sung by a choir whose performers on the night did not outnumber the choir whose members suffered from mince pie malady. The latter choir was a male-voice choir.

4. When Tinsel Troop had been practicing for the final time before their grand performance, some of the elves had taken the choirmaster's instruction of wearing a lot of tinsel around their necks to the extreme – and almost choked on it. Fortunately, no long-term harm was done and seven fewer members than the elves acquiring ice dance fever while ice skating were left with tinsellitis.

5. Some members of the choir whose task was to decorate the music hall with mistletoe were struck by mistletoe malaise. If these were members of Poinsettia Posse, there were seven members who'd become ill. If, instead, these were members of the choir whose first song in their medley was *Freeze a Jolly Good Fellow*, this choir was the all-male choir.

6. The combined number of ill elves belonging to Roasted Chestnuts and the choir whose first song in their medley was *All I Want for Christmas Is Food* was thirty more elves than the ill elves in the choir whose first song in their medley was *All the Jingle Ladies*. None of these choirs were struck by mistletoe malaise.

	All I Want for Christmas Is Food	All the Jingle Ladies	Freeze a Jolly Good Fellow	Jingle Bell Sock	Santa Claus Is Humming, "Calm Down."	Figgy pudding feebleness	Ice dance fever	Mince pie malady	Mistletoe malaise	Tinsellitis	4	9	13	16	20
Choir Lil' Drummer Dudettes															
Mistletoe Mania															
Poinsettia Posse															
Roasted Chestnuts															
Tinsel Troop															
Healthy elves 4															
9															
13															
16															
20															
Illness Figgy pudding feebleness															
Ice dance fever															
Mince pie malady															
Mistletoe malaise															
Tinsellitis															

Choir	First song	Illness	Healthy elves
Lil' Drummer Dudettes			
Mistletoe Mania			
Poinsettia Posse			
Roasted Chestnuts			
Tinsel Troop			

12. I Only Have Ice for You

Aretha Holly, the Most Distinguished Head Editor of the Elf Press, was typesetting the latest issue of *The Elf Observer*. She was doing the task herself as all her regular staff were off sick due to Christmas carol contagion and she wasn't sure if the apprentices would do the job properly. One topic she was particularly excited about was the announcement of the winner of the annual *I Only Have Ice for You* ice sculpting competition and featuring the five best ice sculptures. Using the clues and the diagram, can you work out the ranking of each ice sculpture, what the judges' comments were, and where on the newspaper page the photos of these exceptional sculptures were positioned?

1. The judging panel consisted of twelve kids whose task was not only to consider how impressive the ice sculptures looked, but to also determine how well they functioned as kids' play equipment. Although *An Elfie Stick*, a solitary climbing pole, was ranked two places lower than the sculpture featuring thirty intertwined bears that formed a maze, one of the judges, nevertheless, was impressed by its modern idea and deemed it "Un-fir-gettable".

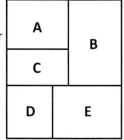

2. As the winning sculpture was quite tall, Aretha Holly placed its photo in a section that was in portrait orientation. The judges didn't think that "The myrrh the merrier" was an apt description for it.

3. The photos of *Christmas Fishes* (a sculpture where a huge trampoline was fastened so that it looked like twelve fish were holding it in their mouths) and the sculpture that, according to the judges, deserved "A round of Santa-plause" touched the section where the photo of the fifth-ranking sculpture was placed.

4. "The myrrh the merrier" and "Love at frost sight" were not heard in connection with sculptures that contained either thirty or twelve icy elements.

5. *Kissing under the Mistletoad* featured a giant toad under whose chin two swings had been attached. The kids placed this sculpture one place higher than the sculpture whose photo was right above the bear-themed *Bear-y Christmas!*

6. *No Time Like the Present* consisted of twenty present-shaped cubes that were hollow and the kids could crawl between them via tunnels. The photo of this masterpiece was not adjacent to the photo of the sculpture that came fourth. Both of them touched the section where the photo of the third-ranking sculpture was positioned.

7. Of the two sculptures consisting of only one icy element, one came first and the other's photo was in Section E.

		Page section					Ranking					Comment				
		A	B	C	D	E	1st	2nd	3rd	4th	5th	"A round of Santa-plause"	"Love at frost sight"	"Santamental"	"The myrrh the merrier"	"Un-fir-gettable"
Sculpture	An Elfie Stick															
	Bear-y Christmas!															
	Christmas Fishes															
	Kissing under the Mistletoad															
	No Time Like the Present															
Comment	"A round of Santa-plause"															
	"Love at frost sight"															
	"Santamental"															
	"The myrrh the merrier"															
	"Un-fir-gettable"															
Ranking	1st															
	2nd															
	3rd															
	4th															
	5th															

Sculpture	Page section	Ranking	Comment
An Elfie Stick			
Bear-y Christmas!			
Christmas Fishes			
Kissing under the Mistletoad			
No Time Like the Present			

13. Elf and Safety

Last week was a busy one for Brave Dave, the Head of the Elf and Safety Department. In addition to his usual workload – which was increasing exponentially by the day in the run up to Christmas – he had meetings with five Elf and Safety Managers. Using the clues, can you figure out when each meeting took place, what each Elf and Safety Manager's area of responsibility was, and what the issue discussed in each meeting concerned?

1. Brave Dave was annoyed that he had to meet two elves in his office over the weekend. Earlier in the week he had caught one of them, yet again, on a ladder taking elfies – despite fully well knowing that ladder safety had its ups and downs – and requested her presence in his office three days later. He had to admonish the other elf for not mistletoeing the line: he had posted inappropriate posters around the place. This was the second time he had to explain that slogans such as "Don't get hurt or you'll get fired." and "Crushed hands or missing fingers may affect your chances of winning a snowball fight." were not in line with how Santa wanted any of the safety messages to be phrased.

2. Bearly Careless, who certainly didn't lack elf confidence, was seen by Brave Dave the day before the elf who was in charge of the Excellent Elf School's safety procedures.

3. The elf whose job it was to make sure that the Quizmas Committee remained safe while preparing for the forthcoming Quizmas Event saw his colleague on a ladder taking elfies as he walked out of Brave Dave's office.

4. If Kinda Mindless was in no need of elf improvement, he met Brave Dave on Thursday. If, instead, Knot Reckless was seen by Brave Dave on the day after Les Lawless, Knot Reckless was the Elf and Safety Manager of the Reindeer Grooming Bureau.

5. The lack of elf discipline was discussed in Brave Dave's office earlier in the week than the lack of elf confidence.

6. Brave Dave felt sorry for the manager who was in need of elf improvement. Ultimately, she was the most conscientious of all the managers, and he hoped that this meeting – which took place later in the week than the meeting with the Elf and Safety Manager of the Elf Press – would help her.

7. Teeny Thoughtless and Bearly Careless did not have an issue with mistletoeing the line. Neither were they involved in enforcing any safety procedures regarding reindeer grooming.

8. Two elves who both had names with the first name and family name sharing the same initial letter were seen by Brave Dave five days apart.

		Elf Press	Engineering Unit	Excellent Elf School	Quizmas Committee	Reindeer Grooming Bureau	Lacked elf confidence	Lacked elf discipline	Needed elf improvement	Too busy taking elfies	Wasn't mistletoeing the line	Monday	Tuesday	Thursday	Saturday	Sunday
Elf	Bearly Careless															
	Les Lawless															
	Kinda Mindless															
	Knot Reckless															
	Teeny Thoughtless															
Day	Monday															
	Tuesday															
	Thursday															
	Saturday															
	Sunday															
Issue	Lacked elf confidence															
	Lacked elf discipline															
	Needed elf improvement															
	Too busy taking elfies															
	Wasn't mistletoeing the line															

Elf	Responsibility	Issue	Day
Bearly Careless			
Les Lawless			
Kinda Mindless			
Knot Reckless			
Teeny Thoughtless			

14. Stocking Thrillers

The final year students at the Excellent Elf School were undertaking their final practical assessment. Miss Tress, the School's Principal, wanted to test how well the elves could spread goodwill and Christmas spirit. So, she divided the class into five teams and asked each to make a Christmas stocking, fill it with a suitable book, and secretly deliver it to an inconspicuous location in a nearby village under the cover of darkness. A lucky villager would find it the following morning and the highly-skilled examiner elves would report the extent of delight on each recipient's face. Using the clues and the drawing, can you work out which stocking by the fireplace was made by each team, what they contained, and where they were delivered later on?

1. After each team finished making their stocking and filled it with a carefully chosen book, they put the stockings in front of Santa's festive fireplace to wait until midnight. When Stocking Squad saw that Jingle Jangles' stocking looked suspiciously identical to theirs, they accused Jingle Jangles of stealing their design.

2. When an old man in Myrrhakesh found *Dr. Snow* in a stocking inside his favorite horse's stable, he looked rather puzzled. He admired the stocking – or possibly wondered about the blobs of dried glue bulging through the seams – before hanging it on the stable wall.

3. Either *The Sleigh of Silence* or *Polar Jar* was found by a little girl at the edge of a village green. If it was the former, it was Rudolph's Rebels who deposited a stocking in Firling. If it was the latter, this book had been placed inside a knitted stocking.

4. The sum of the place numbers of the two stockings in which *One Flew over the Yuletide Guest* and the book chosen by Naughty Nutcrackers were hidden was two numbers lower than the place number of the stocking that ended up in Sleigh-Jing.

5. More Bells Than Whistles' stocking was farther right in front of Santa's fireplace than the stocking that ended up in Budafest. Neither contained *The Hunt for Red Pullover*.

6. None of the elves in the three teams whose stockings were adorned with stripes could knit. Instead, they used a sewing maching as well as super glue when creating their masterpieces. The crocheted stocking was closer to the decorative Christmas tree than the stocking that contained *The Hunt for Red Pullover*.

7. It was the knitted stocking that Miss Tress thought was the most expertly made. Furthermore, she received a super report from an examiner elf who witnessed the recipient's reaction in Greenstown. This team would certainly graduate in the next few days and join Santa's much trusted helpers.

8. The team that used the most super glue placed their stocking (with *Dr. Snow* inside) between the beautifully crocheted stocking and the stocking that later found its way to Firling.

9. Jingle Jangles took their stocking to a village whose name came alphabetically earlier than where the knitted stocking was taken.

		Book					Place no.					Village				
		Dr. Snow	*One Flew over the Yuletide Guest*	*Polar Jar*	*The Hunt for Red Pullover*	*The Sleigh of Silence*	1	2	3	4	5	Budafest	Firling	Greenstown	Myrrhakesh	Sleigh-Jing
Team	Jingle Jangles															
	More Bells Than Whistles															
	Naughty Nutcrackers															
	Rudolph's Rebels															
	Stocking Squad															
Village	Budafest															
	Firling															
	Greenstown															
	Myrrhakesh															
	Sleigh-Jing															
Place no.	1															
	2															
	3															
	4															
	5															

Team	Book	Place no.	Village
Jingle Jangles			
More Bells Than Whistles			
Naughty Nutcrackers			
Rudolph's Rebels			
Stocking Squad			

15. Merry Quizmas

Professor Quiz Whitty, the Quizmas Quiz Grand Master, was delighted that this year ten teams had signed up for the Quizmas Event. He was certain that the participating elves had been preparing all year in order to improve their Quizmas knowledge and to sew their costumes – which were a prerequisite for every team taking part. This year the quiz consisted of thirty carefully crafted questions. Professor Quiz Whitty was overjoyed to announce that there were five teams who only got one question wrong, and whom he, therefore, had the pleasure of crowning joint winners. Using the clues and the professor's questions, can you figure out which team got which question wrong, what the teams' costumes were, and at which table each team sat?

1. Since there was a tie between five teams, Professor Quiz Whitty decided to award an additional trophy for the team with the best costumes. Although Quizzly Bears' outfits were cute, dressing up as polar bears was a rather predictable choice, and so, they didn't win this much-coveted trophy.

2. The team that sat closest to Santa's fireplace got the question relating to sharks wrong. This question's number was lower than the sum of the table numbers of Hark the Herald Angels Win and the team dressed up as Christmas puddings.

3. Professor Quiz Whitty presented his thirty expertly devised questions in a way that they got progressively more difficult as the Quizmas Quiz went on. He had expected the teams to stumble at the last question but, surprisingly, everyone knew that the answer to "Why don't you ever see Santa in the hospital?" was "Because he has private elf care." The team that won the trophy for the best costume got a question wrong in the earlier half, rather than the latter half, of the competition.

4. Unlike the other teams, Les Quizerables and the team with the pinecone outfits helped each other design and sew their costumes. The sum of their table numbers was ten less than the sum of the question numbers they got wrong. The pictures on these two question cards were not painted or stencilled.

5. It was Professor Quiz Whitty's endearing habit to draw festive pictures on the index cards he used for reading his fiendish questions from. The question accompanied by a pencil drawing of a teddy bear was not the question that Quizmas Crackers got wrong.

6. The team that was farthest from the fireplace complained that the reason they got a question wrong was because they felt so cold. Professor Quiz Whitty pointed out that their excessively bulky penguin outfits would have kept anyone warm, if not boiling hot, and this was just a poor excuse. He had been tempted to award this team the trophy for the best costumes, but due to their whining, he chose the team whose table number was three numbers lower than the table number of the team that, of the five winning teams, got the most difficult question wrong.

7. Of the two teams that didn't know the answers to the questions written on the index cards with a painted moon and a stencilled bauble, one team's table number was five numbers higher than the other team's table number.

8. The two index cards with crayon drawings were Professor Quiz Whitty's favorites. These questions were the ones that the teams that sat the closest to and farthest from the fireplace got wrong. The sum of these two teams' table numbers was thirteen.

9. The costume trophy winners sat at a table whose number was two numbers higher than the table number of the team that wrongly answered a question that was written on a card with a painted picture on it.

10. The Noel-It-Alls wore either the snowball or the Christmas pudding costumes. If they wore the former, they got the question relating to the gingerbread man wrong. If they wore the latter, they sat at Table 6.

11. Quizmas Crackers, who sat closest to the fireplace, were sure that they would win the competition. Although they were happy with the shared five-way win, they were disappointed that they didn't win the additional costume trophy, despite having collaborated with the sewing experts in the Les Quizerables team.

7. Why shouldn't you mess with the gingerbread man? He's a tough cookie.

9. What did the sea say to Santa? Nothing – it just waved.

11. Who delivers presents to baby sharks at Christmas? Santa Jaws.

18. Why can't Christmas trees knit? They always drop their needles.

27. What is the best Christmas present? A broken drum – you just can't beat it.

		Question no.					Costume					Table no.				
		7	9	11	18	27	Christmas puddings	Penguins	Pinecones	Polar bears	Snowballs	1	3	5	6	8
Team	Hark the Herald Angels Win															
	Les Quizerables															
	Quizmas Crackers															
	Quizzly Bears															
	The Noel-It-Alls															
Table no.	1															
	3															
	5															
	6															
	8															
Costume	Christmas puddings															
	Penguins															
	Pinecones															
	Polar bears															
	Snowballs															

Team	Question no.	Costume	Table no.
Hark the Herald Angels Win			
Les Quizerables			
Quizmas Crackers			
Quizzly Bears			
The Noel-It-Alls			

16. Up to Snow Good

It was another day of heavy snowfall and the elves in Santa's workshop were looking for some excitement. They had been working hard to get all the presents ready for Christmas (although they were by no means finished), and their lunch hour seemed like the perfect time to have a snowball fight. So they donned their winter coats, mittens, and scarves before heading outside. Unfortunately, some of the elves weren't very accurate at throwing snowballs and accidentally hit some passers-by. Using the clues, can you work out whose snowball hit which passing elf, at what time, and what the consequence of each misfired snowball was?

1. The snowball fight started as soon as the elves were outdoors, one minute after the lunchtime bells jingled. It was two minutes after the snowball fight's start time that Professor Quiz Whitty was hit on his arm.

2. The elves who were accidentally hit by snowballs were authority figures within Santa's household. Each of them decided what the disciplinary action should be for the elf whose snowball had walloped them. Of the elves whose snowballs landed on uninteded targets one minute apart, one of them was told to go to bed early and miss watching the northern lights that night. This was not Carol Swinger whose unwitting target got hit earlier than the elf who was at the receiving end of a snowball behind Santa's workshop.

3. Of the two elves who were hit by snowballs at the Excellent Elf School's entrance, the one who was hit later told the snowball thrower to stand in front of a mirror and give herself a good elf talk.

4. As she was stepping out of the Excellent Elf School's entrance, Miss Tress quickly ducked down. However, she wasn't fast enough and instantly felt a thump on her forehead.

5. Carol Springer's snowball hit an elf who was just about to enter the Excellent Elf School. This was two minutes earlier than when a snowball hit Angie Near behind Santa's workshop.

6. Carol Bringer hit a passer-by on her back. She was not the recipient of Professor Quiz Whitty's disciplinary action that involved saluting the reindeer for the rest of the afternoon.

7. If the lunchtime bells jingled at 1 pm, it was Carol Winger who was asked to do a good deed. If, instead, the lunchtime bells jingled at 13:01, it was Angie Near who was hit at 13:11.

8. Aretha Holly, who would never deny anyone the pleasure of watching the northern lights, was hit by a snowball earlier than both the elf who advocated that and the elf who was disappointed by the young elves' inability to aim and, therefore, ordered the snowball thrower to do target practice for two hours.

		Angie Near	Aretha Holly	Brave Dave	Miss Tress	Professor Quiz Whitty	13:03	13:06	13:07	13:09	13:11	Early bedtime	Elf talk in front of mirror	Good deed	Saluting reindeer	Target practice
Elf	Carol Bringer															
	Carol Slinger															
	Carol Springer															
	Carol Swinger															
	Carol Winger															
Consequence	Early bedtime															
	Elf talk in front of mirror															
	Good deed															
	Saluting reindeer															
	Target practice															
Time	13:03															
	13:06															
	13:07															
	13:09															
	13:11															

Elf	Hit by snowball	Time	Consequence
Carol Bringer			
Carol Slinger			
Carol Springer			
Carol Swinger			
Carol Winger			

17. Letter Safe than Sorry

Last night's blizzard was over. Santa was sitting in front of the fireplace, drinking Christmas thyme tea and eating sneakily acquired frosted sugar cookies. The maintenance elves were busy clearing the worst of the snow while Santa was perusing this week's mail. There were five letters that caught his eye, mainly because of their opening sentences. Using the clues, can you figure out who sent which letter, from where, and what their arrival days were?

1. Santa noticed that all the letters had been sent from nearby locations that were dotted along the road to the top of Ear Fell. He knew this winding road well as, quite quirkily, the place names followed a reverse alphabetical order starting from Zest Zone's lowest altitude location to the highest peak called Angel Apex. Along the way, there were two highly rated snack stops, Butterscotch Base and Plum Pudding Place. He quite liked to frequent both.

2. Santa made a note to contact Snale Male, the Head of the Elf Mail, in order to ask why the local letters had to go first all the way to the sorting hub in Parcelona rather than have his Elvesdropping Elves collect them while on duty? Currently it was taking two days for the letters to arrive and Santa felt it was too long. Santa also wanted to remind him that he really should stop telling jokes about undelivered letters as no one seemed to get them, and instead, concentrate on improving his delivery.

3. The letter from Hot Chocolate Hill arrived one day earlier than when the letter that said, "Dear Santa, I hope Rudolph eats the naughty list." was put in the Elf Mail. One of these letter writers had the letter O in their first name and the other in their last name.

4. It was either Jay Walker or Joe King whose letter was posted on Monday. If it was Jay Walker's letter, he sent his letter from a place that was lower down on Ear Fell than Plum Pudding Place. If, instead, it was Joe King's letter, he wrote, "Dear Santa, it is too late now to say sorry?"

5. Don Keigh sent his letter to Santa on the same day as when the letter that said, "Dear Santa, the elves did it." was received. The former was sent from a lower altitude than Quince Pie Quarter and the latter was sent from Nutcracker Nook.

6. The letter from Sugarplum Station arrived one day later than the letter saying, "Dear Santa, I can explain." If either of these letters was written by Kay Oss, the latter letter came from Candle County.

7. Dinah Mite didn't write, "Dear Santa, please define nice." She put her letter in the Elf Mail higher up on Ear Fell than where the letter that arrived on Monday came from.

8. Don Keigh's letter arrived earlier than the letter from Candle County.

		Dear Santa...					Location					Arrival day				
		I can explain	I hope Rudolph eats the naughty list	is it too late now to say sorry	please define nice	the elves did it	Candle County	Hot Chocolate Hill	Nutcracker Nook	Sugarplum Station	Toboggan Town	Monday	Tuesday	Wednesday	Thursday	Friday
Name	Dinah Mite															
	Don Keigh															
	Jay Walker															
	Joe King															
	Kay Oss															
Arrival day	Monday															
	Tuesday															
	Wednesday															
	Thursday															
	Friday															
Location	Candle County															
	Hot Chocolate Hill															
	Nutcracker Nook															
	Sugarplum Station															
	Toboggan Town															

Name	Dear Santa...	Location	Arrival day
Dinah Mite			
Don Keigh			
Jay Walker			
Joe King			
Kay Oss			

18. Candle with Care

It was the responsiblity of the Excellent Elf School's first-year students to keep all the paths in Santa's village well lit after dark. This year's students followed the age-old tradition of using ice lanterns as they looked magical against the the backdop of the black sky, the moon, the stars, and the playful northern lights. Instead of making just ordinary outdoor candles, though, the students decided to be a little more creative and place candle sculptures inside different shapes of ice lanterns. The five most interesting candles were positioned near Santa's favorite tree, behind the library. Using the clues and the picture, can you work out which candle was placed inside which shape of ice lantern, what each candle's burning time was, and where these lanterns were positioned?

1. The candles near Santa's favorite tree behind the library were along the path that runs from Santa's workshop in the east to the Excellent Elf School in the west. Although the maintenance elves tried to keep the path clear of snow, it was a difficult task at times. Everytime it snowed heavily it was only the candles that indicated where the path should have been.

2. For centuries the candle-burning time in Santa's village has been measured in microcenturies. Professor May Trix was always eager to help her students understand how microcenturies were translated into hours, minutes, and seconds: each microcentury was one millionth of a century which equalled slightly more than 52 and a half minutes. The students, however, never really reciprocated her enthusiasm. It was not the candle called *Santa Claws* (which depicted a stalking cat) whose burning time was two microcenturies less than the burning time of a candle that was placed inside a cone-shaped ice lantern.

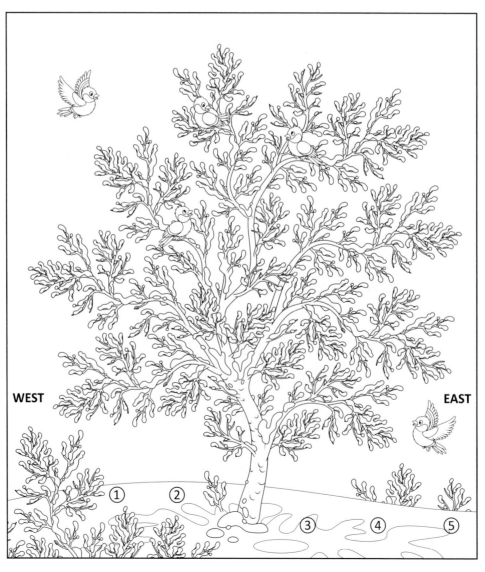

3. *Whisking You a Merry Christmas* was a candle made in the shape of a large whisk standing upright in a mixing bowl. Its burning time was one microcentury less than the candle that was positioned immediately to the west of Santa's favorite tree.

4. The candles whose combined burning time was thirty-five microcenturies weren't positioned next to each other. The one that was closer to the Excellent Elf School was placed inside a sphere-shaped ice lantern.

5. It was the candle that poked well above the ice lantern (even though the brief stated that all candles should fit inside their respective ice structures) that had the longest burning time. This candle was closer to Santa's workshop than the candle whose burning time was three microcenturies less than the candle named *Love You Snow Much* (which depicted two infatuated elves holding hands).

6. *Bah-Hum-Pug*, the candle in the shape of a cute pug dog, was positioned closer to the Excellent Elf School than the candle that was inside the pyramid-shaped ice lantern.

7. If *Christmas Tree Hugger* (a candle in the shape of a Christmas tree that was being hugged by a little elf) didn't fit inside its ice lantern, it was in Position 5. If, instead, it snuggly fitted inside a sphere-shaped ice lantern, it was in Position 3.

8. The two candles with an animal theme were placed inside the cube and the pyramid ice lanterns. The sum of their position numbers was six, which was the same as the sum of the position numbers of the candles that incorporated elves in their designs.

	Ice lantern					Burning time					Position				
	Cone	Cube	Cylinder	Pyramid	Sphere	16 microcenturies	17 microcenturies	19 microcenturies	20 microcenturies	21 microcenturies	1	2	3	4	5
Bah-Hum-Pug															
Christmas Tree Hugger															
Love You Snow Much															
Santa Claws															
Whisking You a Merry Christmas															
1															
2															
3															
4															
5															
16 microcenturies															
17 microcenturies															
19 microcenturies															
20 microcenturies															
21 microcenturies															

Candle name	Ice lantern	Burning time	Position
Bah-Hum-Pug			
Christmas Tree Hugger			
Love You Snow Much			
Santa Claws			
Whisking You a Merry Christmas			

19. Best in Snow

Santa was very proud of his husky training team, and each year the Best in Snow competition allowed them to show off their amazing abilities. In previous years the competition had focused on agility and endurance, but this year Santa wanted to focus on the more creative side of training. Hence, he announced that each trainer elf was to put together a dance routine and perform it with their respective dog. Using the clues, can you figure out which husky was trained by which elf, to which song they performed, and what each pair's ranking was?

1. It was Mrs Claus, Miss Tress, and Aretha Holly who formed the judging panel. While Mrs Claus appreciated fluidity and original dance moves, Miss Tress and Aretha Holly were more interested in seeing tricks. The songs that were danced as foxtrot routines weren't ranked first as their complete lack of tricks didn't impress these two ladies.

2. Of the songs that lent themselves to American smooth dances, one was called *Deck the Halls with Bows on Collies* and the other's creative content was put together by Sugarplum Mary. However, it was the quickstep (danced by a husky with a food-related name) that satisfied all the judges with its fluid, original moves interspersed by plenty of magnificent tricks, and so, it was ranked higher than the American-smooth dances which only contained a few tricks.

3. Perrie Winkle had spent days putting together a beautiful dance routine, only to find out that she and her dog with a red collar would have got a higher score if she'd included some tricks. However, she did better than her best friend who came one place higher than the team that danced to *Go Tail It on the Mountain* (whose choreography didn't contain any tricks).

4. Fruitcake, whose sparkling collar said, "Wishing You a Hairy Christmas and a Yappy New Year!", was ranked lower than the husky whose trainer was Tinker Belle. Neither danced to the song *Dachshund Through the Snow*.

5. Icicle and Mittens were the only dogs who wore red collars. One of them read, "I've been a furry good dog." It was this husky who danced to *Here Comes Santa Paws*.

6. It was a foxtrot that came fourth and an American smooth that came last.

7. *Barking Around the Christmas Tree* was the song to a dance that came two places lower than Chris Tingle's dance. The latter's dog had a red collar without any text written on it.

8. Mary Light, whose husky had a green collar, came one place higher than the elf who had trained Mittens.

		Trainer elf					Song					Ranking				
		Chris Tingle	Mary Light	Perrie Winkle	Sugarplum Mary	Tinker Belle	Barking Around the Christmas Tree	Dachshund Through the Snow	Deck the Halls with Bows on Collies	Go Tail It on the Mountain	Here Comes Santa Paws	1st	2nd	3rd	4th	5th
Husky	Cranberry															
	Fruitcake															
	Icicle															
	Mittens															
	Tiny Tim															
Ranking	1st															
	2nd															
	3rd															
	4th															
	5th															
Song	Barking Around the Christmas Tree															
	Dachshund Through the Snow															
	Deck the Halls with Bows on Collies															
	Go Tail It on the Mountain															
	Here Comes Santa Paws															

Husky	Trainer elf	Song	Ranking
Cranberry			
Fruitcake			
Icicle			
Mittens			
Tiny Tim			

20. Elvesdropping

The Elvesdropping Elves were super busy in the run up to Christmas. Each day they went out in the early hours, traveled to their designated locations, and observed people before coming back late in the day to write their reports before the midnight deadline. Using the clues, can you figure out how many pages each elf's report was yesterday, at what time these reports were submitted to Santa, and which event the elves found the most memorable?

1. Blinker Belle and the elf whose report was eighteen pages long spent the day in Quince Pie Quarter. The latter stayed in the western side of the village and jotted down a good deed by a kid whose attempt at delighting his mom didn't end in the desired outcome.

2. It was in Garland Glen where an elf saw a little girl with ginger hair decorating her brother's bedroom walls with a red crayon. She was clearly drawing Santa Claus and his elves, but sadly, her big brother and parents weren't appreciative of her artistic talents.

3. It was the young twins of the Winterdale family who decided to surprise their dad by cleaning his new laptop: they submerged it in a sink full of soapy water and thoroughly scrubbed it with a nail brush. The elf who saw this (and who wasn't the first one to submit her report, yet managed to do so earlier than Winker Belle) chuckled as she wrote in her report what the dad's face had looked like after he found his laptop drying by the fireplace.

4. The report that included a blow-by-blow account of a brother helpfully cutting his sister's hair very short was submitted earlier than Thinker Belle's report, but later than the report that was three pages shorter than Stinker Belle's report.

5. Of the reports that gave details of events that took place in Feast Field and Snowfall Square, one was twenty-one pages long and the other was submitted at 11.37 pm.

6. Clinker Belle's report was three pages shorter than the report that was submitted less than a quarter of an hour before midnight.

7. The elf who witnessed a little girl using white finger paint to create a snowy forest scene on her mom's car door submitted her report more than ten minutes later than when the twenty-three-page report was submitted.

8. The longest and the shortest reports were submitted less than ten minutes apart. One of them contained a humorous description of a haircut.

9. The elf whose most memorable event in Snowfall Square was of a car being painted wrote her report late. She submitted it only thirteen minutes before the midnight deadline. This was not Thinker Belle whose report about Garland Glen's inhabitants was four pages longer.

		Event					No. of pages					Time				
		Cutting sister's hair	Decorating brother's room	Painting mom's car	Preparing mom's bath	Washing dad's laptop	18	21	23	25	28	23:28	23:29	23:37	23:39	23:47
Elf	Blinker Belle															
	Clinker Belle															
	Stinker Belle															
	Thinker Belle															
	Winker Belle															
Time	23:28															
	23:29															
	23:37															
	23:39															
	23:47															
No. of pages	18															
	21															
	23															
	25															
	28															

Elf	Event	No. of pages	Time
Blinker Belle			
Clinker Belle			
Stinker Belle			
Thinker Belle			
Winker Belle			

21. A Deery Atmosphere

Capture Crew, the Excellent Elf School's photography club, was running a competition: Whoever took the most stunning photo of the northern lights would get the much-coveted prize of a masterclass with Cam Era. Five elves sharing a room in the Elves' Restful Residence went out one night when the sky was clear. Despite each elf having a special technique that they hoped would get them that winning snap, their attempts were doomed as the reindeer were hosting their weekly stand-up comedy night and the elves couldn't help but laugh at their jokes, thereby missing their chance of capturing the northern lights. Using the clues and the drawing, can you work out which technique each elf used in an attempt to get the perfect picture, which reindeer's joke each found the funniest, and where on the snowy stage the jocular reindeer were positioned?

1. The elf whose technique was to adjust the camera's focus and use the infinity setting never actually took the camera out of his pocket. He was so mesmerized by Glitter Nose's performance and, in particular, a joke whose answer included the word 'deer'.

2. The elf who laughed most at the performance of the reindeer who was standing next to Sparkle Toes on the same side of the Christmas tree had her pockets full of spare batteries. She had learned the hard way that in freezing temperatures batteries lose power faster than in warmer weather.

3. The two reindeer who stood next to the Christmas tree didn't impress Yule Log that much.

4. The joke involving Rudolph was the one that caused an elf to fall over her tripod. It was not Glamor Coat who told this joke.

5. Twinkle Pose was one of the reindeer who faced away from the Christmas tree.

6. The reindeer whose joke made Ridge Tent laugh the most stood closer to the Christmas tree than Silver Throat. The tails of these two reindeer faced each other.

7. The elf who had a spare memory card in her pocket found the joke told by the reindeer standing next to Twinkle Pose the funniest. This was not Gale Force.

8. Aurora Borealis and her brother Frost Bite laughed most at the jokes of reindeer whose first names finished with the letter R. These two reindeer didn't stand next to each other on the snowy stage.

9. The elf who intended to use a wide-angle lens was most impressed by the reindeer whose best joke was about Christmas tree decorations.

10. Gale Force laughed most at the joke involving Mrs Claus. The reindeer who told this joke stood next to Glitter Nose.

		Technique					Reindeer					Position				
		Infinity focus	Spare batteries	Spare memory card	Tripod	Wide-angle lens	Glamor Coat	Glitter Nose	Silver Throat	Sparkle Toes	Twinkle Pose	A	B	C	D	E
Elf	Aurora Borealis															
	Gale Force															
	Frost Bite															
	Ridge Tent															
	Yule Log															
Position	A															
	B															
	C															
	D															
	E															
Reindeer	Glamor Coat															
	Glitter Nose															
	Silver Throat															
	Sparkle Toes															
	Twinkle Pose															

Elf	Technique	Reindeer	Place
Aurora Borealis			
Gale Force			
Frost Bite			
Ridge Tent			
Yule Log			

22. The Knotty List

The students at the Excellent Elf School were required to learn a number of different knots each year and the Knotty Knot Exam every December tested the elves' knot mastery. Unfortunately, there were five elves who each failed to tie one of the knots included in their 'Knots to Be Mastered' list. Hence, they had to undertake Professor Knot-a-Lot's remedial class. Using the clues and the drawing, can you work out which elf had to learn which knot, what each elf's excuse was for not passing their exam in the first place, and which time period they each spent in the remedial class?

1. Professor Knot-a-Lot staggered the start times of his remedial class so that Year 1 students arrived first at 4 pm and Year 2 students arrived fifteen minutes later. 4.30 pm was the start time of a Year 3 student. The senior students had learned by now that there was no getting away from learning their knots, and in fact, it was better to do it when they were supposed to and not go through Professor Knot-a-Lot's somewhat embarrassing 4-step learning process.

2. Of the two students who had visited the gourmet kitchen's pantry in order to have a midnight snack before the Knotty Knot Exam the following morning, the one who managed to escape before Mrs Claus locked the pantry's door was not a Year 1 student.

3. The bow tie was included in the Year 1 curriculum. This was something that Carole Singer had mastered the previous year.

4. If she hadn't found it so difficult to figure out how to make a song and dance about her knot (of all the elves in the remedial class, she spent the longest doing this step), Leigh Way would have finished earlier than the elf who had been playing ice hockey instead of revising for their exam.

5. The student whose song-and-dance number consisted of a boogie to the tune of *Neigh Bells Ring* was a second year student.

THE 4-STEP PROCESS

1. Theoretical learning
2. Practice & repetition
3. Make a song and dance about the knot
4. Show to Professor Knot-a-Lot

6. The student who spent the longest on the practice-and-repetition step was also the one who spent the most time in Professor Knot-a-Lot's remedial class. Her excuse for not learning all the knots was that she had spent so much time petting reindeer.

7. Of the elves who spent the same amount of time in the remedial class, one of them (who started the class fifteen minutes earlier than Pixie Crop) rapped to the tune of *Who Let the Elves Out* while performing a dance about her knot.

8. It was the elf who finished the remedial class fifteen minutes after the elf who had been learning the manger hitch who got trapped in the pantry and didn't get out until the exam had already started. Mind you, even if she had been there in time, she wouldn't have passed the exam. Even in the remedial class she was not the one who spent the least amount of time to get through Professor Knot-a-Lot's 4-step learning process – unlike her best friend with whom she had shared the midnight snack adventure.

9. The elf who was late for the Knotty Knot Exam because she got tangled in fairy lights was disappointed to have to take part in the remedial class. She comforted herself by telling herself that she already knew how to tie the icicle hitch and the quick release knot even though she was in a lower year group than when these knots were taught.

10. It was not Round Robyn who had a midnight snack in the gourmet kitchen's pantry. The two elves who did share this adventure didn't start their remedial class at the same time, nor was their finish time the same.

11. The elves who incorporated *Neigh Bells Ring* and *Who Let the Elves Out* into their performances learned the package tying knot and the manger hitch (but not necessarily in this order) during their remedial class.

12. The elf who failed the Knotty Knot Exam due falling asleep (no doubt because she had stayed up so late) was the one who got through Professor Knot-a-Lot's 4-step process the fastest.

13. Of the elves who spent the longest doing Steps 2 and 3, one practiced tying the quick release knot and the other one was called Round Robyn.

14. Carole Singer finished the remedial class earlier than the elf who used the song *Neigh Bells Ring* in her performance.

		Knot					Time in class					Excuse				
		Bow tie	Icicle hitch	Manger hitch	Package tying knot	Quick release knot	16:00 – 18:15	16:00 – 18:45	16:15 – 18:15	16:15 – 18:30	16:30 – 18:45	Fell asleep	Petting reindeer	Playing ice hockey	Tangled in fairy lights	Trapped in pantry
Elf	Carole Singer															
	Leigh Way															
	Mary Tale															
	Pixie Crop															
	Round Robyn															
Excuse	Fell asleep															
	Petting reindeer															
	Playing ice hockey															
	Tangled in fairy lights															
	Trapped in pantry															
Time in class	16:00 – 18:15															
	16:00 – 18:45															
	16:15 – 18:15															
	16:15 – 18:30															
	16:30 – 18:45															

Elf	Knot	Time in class	Excuse
Carole Singer			
Leigh Way			
Mary Tale			
Pixie Crop			
Round Robyn			

23. Gangsta Wrappers

Noel Mischief, the hip hop society at the Excellent Elf School, entered five enthusiastic wrappers into Santa's annual Rustle. The Rustle was a much-anticipated competition where the competitors had to design festive wrapping paper, make it from scratch, and then wrap a gift of their choice to showcase their creations as well as their wrapping skills. It was Elfred Hitchcock, the President of Noel Mischief, who brought the wrapped presents to the judges' table so that the masterpieces could be judged anonymously. Using the clues and the drawing, can you figure out the theme of each elf's wrapping paper, how long it took for them to design and make their creations, and which present in the arms of Elfred Hitchcock was wrapped by which elf?

1. It was only the five Noel Mischief members who took part in this year's Rustle. Perhaps the other elves were intimidated by their competitive edge. After all, they had been wrapping all year round. It was the two cousins who had collaborated in writing the lyrics for their hit song *Rebel without a Claus* who were the fastest to finish their tasks.

2. A present that was closer to Elfred Hitchcock's right hand (and did not have a red velvet ribbon) than the present which was wrapped in Glad Slidings themed wrapping paper contained a Santa Claus action doll. The elf who wrapped the action doll took less time than the Glad Slidings creator to submit his entry.

3. Elf Pacino spent less time on his entry than the elf whose wrapping paper depicted frolicking horses in the snow.

4. The wrapping paper that was complemented by a red velvet ribbon was the creation of the elf who took longer to create his present than Elf Capone, but not as long as the elf who wrapped a handbag inside Present B.

5. Of the two wrapping paper patterns that portrayed animals, one was created by Elf Costello's younger brother and the other was created by Elf Costello's older brother. The former was farther away from Elfred Hitchcock's left hand than the latter. It was the eldest brother who was a collaborator in the song *Rebel without a Claus*.

6. A dark green satin ribbon was incorporated into the wrapping paper themed A December to Remember. Instead of making a pretty bow out of the ribbon, this elf had glued it onto the paper, making his wrapping paper stripy. The judges weren't quite sure why anyone would remember such an unimaginative pattern wrapped around Present D.

7. Elfy Kimber spent longer creating his competition entry than the elf who created the Pine-ing for You wrapping paper (which depicted a fir tree forest). The difference between these two elves' creation times was less than ten minutes. These elves' presents touched each other in Elfred Hitchcock's arms.

8. Who Deers Wins portrayed a herd of deer around a Christmas tree while Glad Slidings showed little elflings sliding around on a frozen lake. The presents that were wrapped inside these wrapping papers were not decorated with a red ribbon. Nor did they touch each other in the arms of Elfred Hitchcock.

9. The present that touched all the other presents in Elfred Hitchcock's arms took seven minutes less time to submit than the present of a handbag.

10. The presents wrapped by Elf Capone's two older brothers were closer to Elfred Hitchcock's left hand than Elf Capone's present. It took him over two hours to finish his creation.

11. Of the Santa action doll present and the present whose wrapping paper incorporated the green satin ribbon, one was created the fastest and the other by one of Elf Pacino's younger brothers.

			Present					Theme					Time				
			A	B	C	D	E	A December to Remember	Glad Slidings	Mare-y Christmas	Pine-ing for You	Who Deers Wins	1 h 47 mins	1 h 52 mins	2 h 7 mins	2 h 11 mins	2 h 18 mins
Elf		Elf Capone															
		Elf Costello															
		Elfie Solomons															
		Elf Pacino															
		Elfy Kimber															
Time		1 h 47 mins															
		1 h 52 mins															
		2 h 7 mins															
		2 h 11 mins															
		2 h 18 mins															
Theme		A December to Remember															
		Glad Slidings															
		Mare-y Christmas															
		Pine-ing for You															
		Who Deers Wins															

Elf	Present	Theme	Time
Elf Capone			
Elf Costello			
Elfie Solomons			
Elf Pacino			
Elfy Kimber			

24. Easier Sleigh'd Than Done

It was early morning on Christmas Eve. Yule Befine, Santa's Chief Personal Assistant, was in charge of making sure Rudolph's sleigh was packed and ready for Santa's imminent departure. She asked five of her trainee members of staff to pack the sleigh and gave them a diagram to show them where the different items should be placed. Unfortunately, the trainee elves weren't quite up to the job and not everything ended up where it should have. Using the clues and the diagram, can you work out which elf packed which items, where the items were supposed to have been packed, and where they actually ended up?

1. Yule Befine expected each trainee elf to pack the items they were responsible for according to her instructions. The elf whose task it was to stack the presents into the sleigh was the only one who placed them where they should be: in the area behind the bench.

2. Of the items that were supposed to have been packed on the right-hand side of the sleigh, one should have been packed by Hansen Pockets and the other item was the Very Important Maps satchel.

3. Henny Questions discovered that the place that had been reserved for her was already in use by the time she got to the sleigh. Consequently, she decided to use another compartment. This compartment's number was higher than the compartment number that she had originally been allocated.

4. The sum of the intended place numbers where Joanna Hand and Hansen Pockets were supposed to have packed their items was the same as the sum of the compartment numbers where the Very Important Maps satchel and the snacks consisting of carrots for Rudolph and gingerbread cookies for Santa ended up.

5. The Christmas sweater, which was to keep Santa warm if he started to feel chilly as he was traveling, ended up in a compartment that had been meant for the very long address list. Neither was packed by Betty B. Ready.

6. The elf whose job it was to pack the presents took the longest to finish her task. She had started already before any of the other elves turned up and remained packing the sleigh after everyone else had finished. She noticed that Anya Tows' allocated compartment was on the right-hand side of the sleigh, but her item ended up on the left-hand side.

7. Joanna Hand and Anya Tows finished packing their items earlier than Henny Questions.

8. The address list ended up closer to the presents than the Christmas sweater.

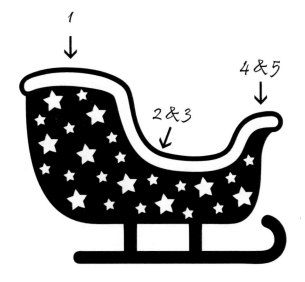

1. Area behind the bench
2. Drawer underneath the bench — right side
3. Drawer underneath the bench — left side
4. Storage cabinet at the front — right side
5. Storage cabinet at the front — left side

9. Joanna Hand put her item in a place that was supposed to have been Hansen Pockets's place, which left Hansen Pockets with a dilemma when he came to pack his item. Instead of reporting this to Yule Befine, he figured that it wasn't that important if the items were not in their allocated places. He put his item in the last empty compartment.

10. Santa was in such a hurry to leave that Yule Befine didn't get a chance to check how well her trainee elves had done the packing. However, since the task wasn't that difficult, she figured that everyone must have done their jobs perfectly and trusted that the snacks were where they were supposed to be: on the left-hand side of the sleigh.

		Essential items					Intended place					Actual place				
		Address list	Carrots & cookies	Christmas sweater	Presents	Very Important Maps satchel	1	2	3	4	5	1	2	3	4	5
Elf	Anya Tows															
	Hansen Pockets															
	Henny Questions															
	Betty B. Ready															
	Joanna Hand															
Actual place	1										
	2										
	3										
	4										
	5										
Intended place	1					
	2					
	3					
	4					
	5					

Elf	Essential items	Intended place	Actual place
Anya Tows			
Hansen Pockets			
Henny Questions			
Betty B. Ready			
Joanna Hand			

25. A Lost Claus

Shortly after Santa had taken off on his annual epic journey to deliver presents all around the world, Mrs Claus went to the library, took *The Count of Monte Christmas* from the bookshelf, and sat down next to the Christmas tree. Suddenly she noticed a cardboard box behind the tree. What was the box doing there? She went to have a look – and her heart sank: All the maps that Santa would need were there! She grabbed the box and alerted the whole household. The members of the Reindeer Affairs Committee harnessed Tinsel Cheeks and five other reindeer in front of Mrs Claus' festive sleigh. Mrs Claus and five senior elves jumped into it and off they went to find Santa. Using the clues, can you figure out what problems Santa faced and in which order, where these problems occurred, what Rudolph said at each adversity, and who helped Santa overcome each problem?

1. Since Santa had done the Christmas journey so many times, he didn't need any maps to start with. It was only at 11.27 pm when he opened the compartment where the Very Important Maps satchel was supposed to be – and discovered that it was not there! He looked into the other compartments in the sleigh and finally found it. He opened the satchel and was shocked: there was not one single map there that would be of any use. The reindeer were galloping forward and, a few minutes later, as they reached a place that they visited immediately before Banquet Berth, Santa had to admit that they were lost without the genuine Very Important Maps.

2. The reason why presents flew off the sleigh and got lost after Santa's visit to Celebration City was because the elf responsible for packing them had not tied the rope knots securely. The problem of slow speed was two-fold: firstly, the reindeer seemed rather unfit and weren't able to sustain the speed needed; and secondly, the sleigh's aerodynamic features weren't working properly. Santa blamed himself for not having supervised the elves or the reindeer sufficiently. Next year the reindeer would have to be fitter and the elves more diligent.

3. Miss Tress was part of the duo who helped to solve the problem that made Rudolph exclaim in despair, "We're swimming against the Yuletide."

4. The elf who had donned a Christmas sweater that depicted snowy evergreen trees wearing detachable Christmas goggles sprang into action sometime after midnight. He gave his partner a pair of goggles so they could look for the lost presents. As luck would have it, the Christmas goggles had been designed to spot presents and the duo found them in no time. Afterwards, they made sure all the presents were tied down using the most secure knots possible.

5. When Rudolph said, "Apply your elf," he was referring to the elf who had filled the kangaroo pouch of his Christmas sweater with candy canes. Santa did not hear this instruction before midnight.

6. It was either in the place immediately before Party Patch or in the place immediately after Soiree Suburb where Santa discovered that the route list that he had been given by Yule Befine was inefficiently planned. This meant that without help he would not be able to deliver all the presents on time. Fortunately, two extremely efficient elves with great organizational skills replanned the rest of the journey for him.

7. The two female elves wore matching sweaters that had skis in their sleeves. Neither had any use for these skis as neither needed to look for lost presents.

8. Festival Field was the second place that Santa visited after midnight.

9. It was not only the relief from Mrs Claus handing the Very Important Maps to Santa, but also the fact that her helper gave the reindeer candy canes from his winter jacket pockets that made Rudolph exclaim, "The best thing since iced gingerbread!"

10. Brave Dave was part of the duo that helped Santa at 11.58 pm. This was in a place that was visited immediately before Celebration City.

11. Of the three places where Santa faced adversities after midnight, one involved rewrapping presents whose wrapping paper had got damaged and another made Rudolph cry, "That was too Claus for comfort."

12. Being the knot expert, Professor Knot-a-Lot's skills were very much needed when he was solving Santa's problem sometime after midnight.

13. It was one of the elves with a Christmas sweater that had skis in its sleeves who heard Rudolph say to Santa, "Don't stop be-leaf-ing," as she was in the process of solving a problem.

14. The elf with the kangaroo-pouch sweater helped Santa after the embarassing incident in Festival Field. His partner was an elf who lent a hand both before and after midnight.

15. Tinsel Cheeks and her fellow reindeer (who were also aspiring stand-up comedians) relieved the slowest of Santa's reindeer of their duty and took over pulling the sleigh. While they were getting organized, Angie Near was tweaking the sleigh's aerodynamic features so that it could travel faster.

16. Santa was delighted that Mrs Claus and her rescue team had come to his aid. Without them Christmas would have been ruined. The whole team followed Santa for the rest of the night – just in case – and there was a mighty cheer when Santa climbed out of the final chimney. Rudolph noticed something on his beard and winked at Mrs Claus. He turned to Santa and said, "That look soots you!"

		Place					Order					Help from					Rudolph said...				
		Banquet Berth	Celebration City	Festival Field	Party Patch	Soiree Suburb	1st	2nd	3rd	4th	5th	Angie Near & Tinsel Cheeks	Elfred Hitchcock & Miss Tress	Miss Tress & Brave Dave	Mrs Claus & Brave Dave	Professor Knot-a-Lot & Mrs Claus	"Apply your elf."	"Don't stop be-leaf-ing."	"That was too Claus for comfort."	"The best thing since iced gingerbread!"	"We're swimming against the Yuletide."
Problem	Damaged wrapping paper																				
	Getting lost																				
	Inefficient route planning																				
	Presents lost																				
	Slow speed																				
Rudolph said...	"Apply your elf."																				
	"Don't stop be-leaf-ing."																				
	"That was too Claus for comfort."																				
	"The best thing since iced gingerbread!"																				
	"We're swimming against the Yuletide."																				
Help from	Angie Near & Tinsel Cheeks																				
	Elfred Hitchcock & Miss Tress																				
	Miss Tress & Brave Dave																				
	Mrs Claus & Brave Dave																				
	Professor Knot-a-Lot & Mrs Claus																				
Order	1st																				
	2nd																				
	3rd																				
	4th																				
	5th																				

Problem	Place	Order	Help from	Rudolph said...
Damaged wrapping paper				
Getting lost				
Inefficient route planning				
Presents lost				
Slow speed				

Solutions

1. Treemendous Decorations

A. Clue 3 indicates that the tree whose theme was Love at First Bite was 55 cm shorter than Holly Wood's tree. When we look at the height options, there is only 1 combination that is feasible: Holly Wood's tree must have been 2 m 80 cm and the tree whose theme was Love at First Bite must have been 2 m 25 cm. Clue 3 also indicates that the tree with the theme Love at First Bite was located in the post office.

Height: 2 m 25 cm = Theme: Love at First Bite = Place: Post office

Elf	Height	Theme	Place
Douglas Fir			
Holly Wood	2 m 80 cm		
Ivy League			
Juniper Berry			
Rosemary Pine			

B. Clue 6 states that of Juniper Berry and Rosemary Pine, one's theme was Tinsel in a Tangle and the other's tree was the shortest. We established in Explanation A that the tree that was 2 m 25 cm – i.e. the shortest tree – was themed Love at First Bite. Therefore, we can express Clue 6 as follows: of Juniper Berry and Rosemary Pine, one's theme was Tinsel in a Tangle and the other's theme was Love at First Bite.

Elf: Juniper Berry = Theme: Love at First Bite OR Tinsel in a Tangle
Elf: Rosemary Pine = Theme: Love at First Bite OR Tinsel in a Tangle

C. Clue 4 compares Douglas Fir's tree to the tree whose theme was Glow-Ho-Ho. This means that Douglas Fir's theme cannot have been Glow-Ho-Ho. Clue 5 indicates that it was a female elf whose theme was the Elphabet. Therefore, Douglas Fir's theme cannot have been the Elphabet since Douglas is a male name. We also established in Explanation B that of Juniper Berry and Rosemary Pine, one's theme was Tinsel in a Tangle and the other's theme was Love at First Bite. Hence, Douglas Fir's theme cannot have been Love at First Bite or Tinsel in a Tangle. It follows from this that his theme must have been Hoppy Holidays.

Clue 1 indicates that the tree with the Hoppy Holidays theme was located in the library. We now know that it was Douglas Fir whose theme was Hoppy Holidays. Therefore, his tree was placed in the library.

Elf	Height	Theme	Place
Douglas Fir		Hoppy Holidays	Library
Holly Wood	2 m 80 cm		
Ivy League			
Juniper Berry			
Rosemary Pine			

D. Clue 5 indicates that the tree whose theme was the Elphabet was located in the Excellent Elf School. We know that Douglas Fir's Hoppy Holidays themed tree was in the library, and that the Love at First Bite themed tree was in the post office (Explanation A). Therefore, of the trees with the themes Glow-Ho-Ho and Tinsel in a Tangle, one must have been located in the gourmet kitchen and the other in the workshop. Clue 2 indicates that the Tinsel in the Tangle themed tree was not in the gourmet kitchen. Hence, it must have been in the workshop. It follows from this that the Glow-Ho-Ho themed tree must have been in the gourmet kitchen.

Theme: Elphabet = Place: Excellent Elf School
Theme: Glow-Ho-Ho = Place: Gourmet kitchen
Theme: Tinsel in a Tangle = Place: Workshop

E. Clue 2 indicates that the tree with the Tinsel in a Tangle theme was more than 20 cm shorter than Ivy League's tree. We know that Holly Wood's tree was 2 m 80 cm. Therefore, Ivy League's tree cannot have been 2 m 80 cm. Also, since Clue 2 indicates that there was a tree that was more than 20 cm shorter than Ivy League's tree, her tree cannot have been 2 m 25 cm or 2 m 35 cm as then it would not be possible for there to be a tree that is more than 20 cm shorter. Furthermore, Clue 7 indicates that the tree in Santa's workshop was decorated by an elf whose last name had 1 more letter than the last name of the elf whose tree was the tallest. This is to say that the last name of the elf who decorated the tallest tree was 1 letter shorter than the last name of the elf whose tree was in the workshop. For the last name of the elf who decorated the Christmas tree to be 1 letter shorter than another elf's last name, it cannot be the longest last name. Since Ivy

League's last name is the longest, her tree cannot have been the tallest, i.e. 3 m 5 cm. It follows from this that Ivy League's tree must have been 2 m 60 cm tall.

We mentioned above that Clue 2 indicates that the tree with the Tinsel in a Tangle theme was more than 20 cm shorter than Ivy League's tree. We now know that Ivy League's tree was 2 m 60 cm. We know from Explanation A that the tree with the theme Love at First Bite was 2 m 25 cm. It follows from this that the tree whose theme was Tinsel in a Tangle must have been 2 m 35 cm tall.

Height: 2 m 35 cm = Theme: Tinsel in a Tangle

Elf	Height	Theme	Place
Douglas Fir		Hoppy Holidays	Library
Holly Wood	2 m 80 cm		
Ivy League	2 m 60 cm		
Juniper Berry			
Rosemary Pine			

F. We know that Holly Wood's tree was 2 m 80 cm tall and Ivy League's tree was 2 m 60 cm tall. We also know from Explanations A and E that the Love at First Bite themed tree was 2 m 25 cm and the Tinsel in a Tangle themed tree was 2 m 35 cm. Explanation B established that these 2 trees were decorated by Juniper Berry and Rosemary Pine (but not necessarily in this order). It follows from this that the height of Douglas Fir's tree must have been 3 m 5 cm.

Elf	Height	Theme	Place
Douglas Fir	3 m 5 cm	Hoppy Holidays	Library
Holly Wood	2 m 80 cm		
Ivy League	2 m 60 cm		
Juniper Berry			
Rosemary Pine			

G. Clue 4 states that there was a 45-centimeter height difference between Douglas Fir's tree and the tree whose theme was Glow-Ho-Ho. We know that Douglas Fir's tree was 3 m 5 cm. Therefore, the tree with the Glow-Ho-Ho theme must have been 2 m 60 cm. We know that this was the height of Ivy League's tree. Hence, Ivy League's theme was Glow-Ho-Ho.

Furthermore, we established in Explanation D that the Glow-Ho-Ho themed tree was located in the gourmet kitchen. It follows from this that Ivy League's tree must have been located there.

Elf	Height	Theme	Place
Douglas Fir	3 m 5 cm	Hoppy Holidays	Library
Holly Wood	2 m 80 cm		
Ivy League	2 m 60 cm	Glow-Ho-Ho	Gourmet kitchen
Juniper Berry			
Rosemary Pine			

H. We know that Douglas Fir's theme was Hoppy Holidays and Ivy League's theme was Glow-Ho-Ho. We also established in Explanation B that Love at First Bite and Tinsel in a Tangle were Juniper Berry and Rosemary Pine's themes (but not necessarily in this order). Therefore, Holly Wood's theme must have been Elphabet. Furthermore, we established in Explanation D that the Elphabet themed tree was located in the Excellent Elf School. Therefore, Holly Wood's tree was in the Excellent Elf School.

Elf	Height	Theme	Place
Douglas Fir	3 m 5 cm	Hoppy Holidays	Library
Holly Wood	2 m 80 cm	Elphabet	Excellent Elf School
Ivy League	2 m 60 cm	Glow-Ho-Ho	Gourmet kitchen
Juniper Berry			
Rosemary Pine			

I. Clue 7 indicates that the tree in Santa's workshop was decorated by an elf whose last name had 1 more letter than the last name of the elf whose tree was the tallest. We know that Douglas Fir's tree was the tallest (3 m 5 cm). His last name has 3 letters. Therefore, the elf whose tree was located in Santa's workshop has 4 letters in their last name. When we look at the name options, there are only 2 elves whose last names have 4 letters: Holly

Wood and Rosemary Pine. However, since Holly Wood's tree was in the Excellent Elf School, it must have been Rosemary Pine whose tree was in the workshop.

Since Douglas Fir's tree was in the library, Holly Wood's tree was in the Excellent Elf School, Ivy League's tree was in the gourmet kitchen, and Rosemary Pine's tree was in the workshop, it must be Juniper Berry's tree that was in the post office.

Elf	Height	Theme	Place
Douglas Fir	3 m 5 cm	Hoppy Holidays	Library
Holly Wood	2 m 80 cm	Elphabet	Excellent Elf School
Ivy League	2 m 60 cm	Glow-Ho-Ho	Gourmet kitchen
Juniper Berry			Post office
Rosemary Pine			Workshop

J. We established in Explanation A that the tree that was 2 m 25 cm was themed Love at First Bite and that it was located in the post office. We now know that Juniper Berry's tree was in the post office. Therefore, her tree must have been 2 m 25 cm and her theme must have been Love at First Bite.

We established in Explanation D that the Tinsel in a Tangle themed tree was in the workshop and in Explanation E that the Tinsel in a Tangle themed tree was 2 m 35 cm tall. We now know that Rosemary Pine's tree was in the workshop. Therefore, her theme must have been Tinsel in a Tangle and her tree's height must have been 2 m 35 cm.

Elf	Height	Theme	Place
Douglas Fir	3 m 5 cm	Hoppy Holidays	Library
Holly Wood	2 m 80 cm	Elphabet	Excellent Elf School
Ivy League	2 m 60 cm	Glow-Ho-Ho	Gourmet kitchen
Juniper Berry	2 m 25 cm	Love at First Bite	Post office
Rosemary Pine	2 m 35 cm	Tinsel in a Tangle	Workshop

2. Rude-olph Awakenings

A. Clue 5 indicates that Perri Patetic will be playing Taylor Drift's songs. Clue 6 indicates that Perrie Odical will be watching *Pear Exports* with the reindeer after waking them up.

Elf	Movie	Musician	Day
Perrie Odical	*Pear Exports*		
Perri Patetic		Taylor Drift	
Perri Stalsis			
Perry Pheral			
Perry Scope			

B. Clue 6 indicates that Perri Odical will be on duty 1 day after when *The Nightwear before Christmas* is shown and 2 days before Perri Patetic will be on duty. This means that Perri Patetic cannot be showing the reindeer *The Nightwear before Christmas* as this movie will be shown earlier in the week. Clue 5 indicates that Perri Patetic won't be showing *Glove Actually* or *The Dough Man* when she's on duty. We also know that the movie on the day when Perrie Odical is on duty will be *Pear Exports*. Therefore, Perri Patetic won't be showing this movie to the reindeer. It follows from this that Perri Patetic will show *The Molar Express* when she is on duty.

Elf	Movie	Musician	Day
Perrie Odical	*Pear Exports*		
Perri Patetic	*The Molar Express*	Taylor Drift	
Perri Stalsis			
Perry Pheral			
Perry Scope			

C. Clue 1 indicates that Beyond Sleigh's songs will be played 2 days before *Pear Exports* is watched. We know that it is Perrie Odical who will be showing *Pear Exports*. This is to say, Beyond Sleigh's songs will be played 2 days before Perrie Odical is on duty. Clue 6 indicates that Perrie Odical will be on duty 2 days before Perri Patetic. When we put these 2 clues together, we can phrase them as follows: Beyond Sleigh's songs will be played one morning, Perrie Odical will be on duty 2 days later, and Perri Patetic will

be on duty 2 days after that. When we look at the day options in the grid, we can see that there is only 1 feasible option: Beyond Sleigh's songs will be played on Wednesday, Perrie Odical will be on duty on Friday, and Perri Patetic will be on duty on Sunday.

Musician: Beyond Sleigh = Day: Wednesday

Elf	Movie	Musician	Day
Perrie Odical	*Pear Exports*		Friday
Perri Patetic	*The Molar Express*	Taylor Drift	Sunday
Perri Stalsis			
Perry Pheral			
Perry Scope			

D. Clue 4 states that Perry Scope and Perri Stalsis will be on duty earlier in the week than when Spruce Springsteen's songs are played. We know that Taylor Drift's songs will be played on Sunday, so it cannot be on Sunday when Spruce Springsteen's songs are played and, hence, Saturday is the latest day when his songs can be played. Since Perry Scope and Perri Stalsis will be on duty before Spruce Springsteen's day, this means that there must be at least 2 days before Spruce Springsteen's songs are played. In other words, his songs cannot be played on Wednesday or Thursday. It follows from this that Spruce Springsteen's songs will be played either on Friday or Saturday.

For Perry Scope and Perri Stalsis to be on duty before Spruce Springsteen's days of Friday or Saturday, they will have to be on duty on Wednesday, Thursday, or Friday. However, since Perrie Odical will be on duty on Friday, it follows that Perry Scope and Perri Stalsis must be on duty on Wednesday and Thursday (but not necessarily in this order).

Since Perry Scope and Perri Stalsis will be on duty on Wednesday and Thursday (but not necessarily in this order), and we know that Perrie Odical will be on duty on Friday and Perri Patetic will be on duty on Sunday, we can deduce that Perry Pheral must be on duty on Saturday.

Elf: Perri Stalsis = Day: Wednesday OR Thursday
Elf: Perry Scope = Day: Wednesday OR Thursday
Musician: Spruce Springsteen = Day: Friday OR Saturday

Elf	Movie	Musician	Day
Perrie Odical	*Pear Exports*		Friday
Perri Patetic	*The Molar Express*	Taylor Drift	Sunday
Perri Stalsis			
Perry Pheral			Saturday
Perry Scope			

E. Clue 3 indicates that if *The Molar Express* is watched earlier in the week than *The Nightwear before Christmas*, the elf on wake-up duty that day will be Perry Pheral; and if, instead, *The Nightwear before Christmas* is watched earlier in the week, Amy Pinehouse's songs will be the wake-up songs on Saturday. We know that *The Molar Express* will be watched on Sunday which is the last day. Therefore, it must be *The Nightwear before Christmas* that will be watched earlier in the week. It follows from this that Amy Pinehouse's songs will be the wake-up songs on Saturday. We know that it is Perry Pheral who will be on duty on Saturday. It follows from this that Perry Pheral will be playing Amy Pinehouse's songs.

Elf	Movie	Musician	Day
Perrie Odical	*Pear Exports*		Friday
Perri Patetic	*The Molar Express*	Taylor Drift	Sunday
Perri Stalsis			
Perry Pheral		Amy Pinehouse	Saturday
Perry Scope			

F. We established in Explanation D that Spruce Springsteen's songs will be played either on Friday or Saturday. We now know that Amy Pinehouse's songs will be played on Saturday. Therefore, Spruce Springsteen's songs will be played on Friday. We know that Perrie Odical will be on duty on Friday. Therefore, it is Perrie Odical who will be playing Spruce Springsteen's songs.

Elf	Movie	Musician	Day
Perrie Odical	*Pear Exports*	Spruce Springsteen	Friday
Perri Patetic	*The Molar Express*	Taylor Drift	Sunday
Perri Stalsis			
Perry Pheral		Amy Pinehouse	Saturday
Perry Scope			

G. Clue 7 states that it is 1 of the elves with the 1st name Perry who will be playing Rudolph's favorite pop star's songs. Clue 1 indicates that Rudolph's favorite pop star is Beyond Sleigh. Therefore, it is either Perry Pheral or Perry Scope who will be playing Beyond Sleigh's songs. We know that Perry Pheral will be playing Amy Pinehouse's songs. Hence, it must be Perry Scope who will be playing Beyond Sleigh's songs.

We established in Explanation C that Beyond Sleigh's songs will be played on Wednesday. Since Perry Scope will be playing Beyond Sleigh's songs, it must be Perry Scope who will be on duty on Wednesday.

Rudolph's favorite pop star = Beyond Sleigh

Elf	Movie	Musician	Day
Perrie Odical	*Pear Exports*	Spruce Springsteen	Friday
Perri Patetic	*The Molar Express*	Taylor Drift	Sunday
Perri Stalsis			
Perry Pheral		Amy Pinehouse	Saturday
Perry Scope		Beyond Sleigh	Wednesday

H. We established in Explanation D that Perri Stalsis will be on duty either on Wednesday or Thursday. Since we now know that Perry Scope will be on duty on Wednesday, Perri Stalsis must be on duty on Thursday.

We know that Perrie Odical will be playing Spruce Springsteen's songs, Perri Patetic will be playing Taylor Drift's songs, Perry Pheral will be playing Amy Pinehouse's songs, and Perry Scope will be playing Beyond Sleigh's songs. It follows from this that it must be Perri Stalsis who will be playing Elfric Clapton's songs.

Elf	Movie	Musician	Day
Perrie Odical	*Pear Exports*	Spruce Springsteen	Friday
Perri Patetic	*The Molar Express*	Taylor Drift	Sunday
Perri Stalsis		Elfric Clapton	Thursday
Perry Pheral		Amy Pinehouse	Saturday
Perry Scope		Beyond Sleigh	Wednesday

I. Clue 6 indicates that Perrie Odical will be on duty 1 day after *The Nightwear before Christmas* is watched. We know that Perrie Odical will be on duty on Friday. Therefore, *The Nightwear before Christmas* will be watched on Thursday. We know that Perri Stalsis will be on duty on Thursday. It follows from this that Perri Stalsis will be entertaining the reindeer with *The Nightwear before Christmas*.

Elf	Movie	Musician	Day
Perrie Odical	*Pear Exports*	Spruce Springsteen	Friday
Perri Patetic	*The Molar Express*	Taylor Drift	Sunday
Perri Stalsis	*The Nightwear before Christmas*	Elfric Clapton	Thursday
Perry Pheral		Amy Pinehouse	Saturday
Perry Scope		Beyond Sleigh	Wednesday

J. We know that Perrie Odical will be showing *Pear Exports*, Perri Patetic will be showing *The Molar Express*, and Perri Stalsis will be showing *The Nightwear before Christmas*. It follows from this that of Perry Pheral and Perry Scope, one will be showing *Glove Actually* and the other *The Dough Man* (but not necessarily in this order). Clue 7 indicates that the elf who will be playing Rudolph's favorite pop star's songs won't be showing the movie *Glove Actually*. We established in Explanation G that Rudolph's favorite pop star is Beyond Sleigh, and we know that Perry Scope will be playing Beyond Sleigh's songs. Therefore, it is not Perry Scope who will be showing *Glove Actually*. It follows from this that it must be Perry Pheral who will be showing *Glove Actually*. Consequently, it must be Perry Scope who will be showing *The Dough Man*.

Elf	Movie	Musician	Day
Perrie Odical	*Pear Exports*	Spruce Springsteen	Friday
Perri Patetic	*The Molar Express*	Taylor Drift	Sunday
Perri Stalsis	*The Nightwear before Christmas*	Elfric Clapton	Thursday
Perry Pheral	*Glove Actually*	Amy Pinehouse	Saturday
Perry Scope	*The Dough Man*	Beyond Sleigh	Wednesday

3. Rolling Out the Dough-Ho-Ho

A. Clue 8 states that Justin Thyme, who was the only male elf participating in the gingerbread house making this year, attempted to make a treehouse. Clue 5 states that *Someone's Barking up the Wrong Christmas Tree* was supposed to have been a treehouse. Therefore, it was Justin Thyme who created *Someone's Barking up the Wrong Christmas Tree*. When we look at the picture, we can see that the elf in Place 5 is standing with the gingerbread house called *Someone's Barking up the Wrong Christmas Tree*. Hence, we can deduce that it must have been Justin Thyme who was in Place 5.

Clue 5 indicates that the repair works for *Someone's Barking up the Wrong Christmas Tree* included copious amounts of super glue. Since Justin Thyme created *Someone's Barking up the Wrong Christmas Tree*, it must have been him who used super glue to fix his gingerbread house.

Elf: Justin Thyme = The only male elf making a gingerbread house

Elf	Place in photo	Accident	Quick fix
Candy Cane			
Cherry Pie			
Hazel Nut			
Justin Thyme	5		Super glue
Maple Syrup			

B. Clue 7 indicates that Cherry Pie's place number was 1 lower than the place number of *What's the Poinsettia?* When we look at the picture, we can see that *What's the Poinsettia?* is in Place 3. It follows from this that Cherry Pie's place number must have been 2.

Clue 1 indicates that the creator of *A Claus Shave* hid the gingerbread house behind a pile of presents. When we look at the picture, we can see that *A Claus Shave* with a pile of presents in front of it is in Place 2. We established above that Cherry Pie was in Place 2. Therefore, it must have been Cherry Pie who resorted to hiding her gingerbread house behind a pile of presents.

Elf	Place in photo	Accident	Quick fix
Candy Cane			
Cherry Pie	2		Hiding behind presents
Hazel Nut			
Justin Thyme	5		Super glue
Maple Syrup			

C. Clue 2 indicates that Hazel Nut handled her gingerbread house's walls a little heavy-handedly and she ended up with wonky walls.

Elf	Place in photo	Accident	Quick fix
Candy Cane			
Cherry Pie	2		Hiding behind presents
Hazel Nut		Wonky walls	
Justin Thyme	5		Super glue
Maple Syrup			

D. We know that Hazel Nut's gingerbread house had wonky walls. Therefore, wonky walls cannot have been the accident that Justin Thyme experienced. Clue 4 indicates that the house that collapsed completely got the quick fix in the form of a plastic dinosaur (so that the devastation would look like it was planned). We know that Justin Thyme used super glue to fix his gingerbread house. Therefore, he cannot have been the one whose house collapsed.

Clue 11 indicates that the gingerbread treehouse wasn't appealing to the reindeer. In other words, the reindeer did not lick off the decorations of the treehouse. We established in Explanation A that it was Justin Thyme who created the gingerbread treehouse. Therefore, it was not his treehouse whose decorations the reindeer licked off.

Clue 9 indicates that the elf whose gingerbread house pieces were burnt was female. We established in Explanation A that Justin Thyme was male. Therefore, he cannot have burnt his gingerbread house pieces. It follows from this that Justin Thyme's gingerbread house's roof must have fallen down.

Accident: Collapsed house = Quick fix: Plastic dinosaur

Elf	Place in photo	Accident	Quick fix
Candy Cane			
Cherry Pie	2		Hiding behind presents
Hazel Nut		Wonky walls	
Justin Thyme	5	Roof fell down	Super glue
Maple Syrup			

E. Clue 3 states that the elf who burnt the gingerbread house pieces was standing directly between Candy Cane and the elf whose creation's roof fell down. We know that it was Justin Thyme whose gingerbread house's roof fell down and that he was in Place 5. Therefore, we can deduce that the elf who burnt the gingerbread house pieces must have stood in Place 4 and Candy Cane must have stood in Place 3.

Place in photo: 4 = Accident: Burnt pieces

Elf	Place in photo	Accident	Quick fix
Candy Cane	3		
Cherry Pie	2		Hiding behind presents
Hazel Nut		Wonky walls	
Justin Thyme	5	Roof fell down	Super glue
Maple Syrup			

F. Clue 10 states that the elf who resorted to turning her house from a 3D construction into a 2D gingerbread picture occupied a place that was 3 numbers higher than the place of the elf who used cardboard scaffolding to prop up her house. Since we know that Justin Thyme occupied Place 5, used super glue, and was male, Place 5 cannot have been where either of these female elves could have been positioned in the photo. It follows from this that there is only 1 combination that makes Clue 10 true: the elf who created a 2D house must have been in Place 4 and the elf who used cardboard scaffolding must have been in Place 1.

Place in photo: 1 = Quick fix: Cardboard scaffolding
Place in photo: 4 = Quick fix: 2D house

G. We know that Candy Cane was in Place 3, Cherry Pie was in Place 2, and Justin Thyme was in Place 5. Therefore, of Hazel Nut and Maple Syrup, one must have been in Place 1 and the other in Place 4. We know that Hazel Nut's accident involved wonky walls. We know from Explanation E that the pieces in the gingerbread house in Place 4 were burnt. Therefore, Hazel Nut cannot have been in Place 4, and it must have been Maple Syrup who was in Place 4. It follows from this that Hazel Nut must have been in Place 1.

Elf	Place in photo	Accident	Quick fix
Candy Cane	3		
Cherry Pie	2		Hiding behind presents
Hazel Nut	1	Wonky walls	
Justin Thyme	5	Roof fell down	Super glue
Maple Syrup	4		

H. We established in Explanation E that the gingerbread house in Place 4 consisted of burnt pieces and in Explanation F that the gingerbread house in Place 4 was turned into a 2D house. We know that Maple Syrup was in Place 4. Therefore, it was her who burnt the gingerbread house pieces and turned it into a 2D house.

We established in Explanation F that the gingerbread house in Place 1 had cardboard scaffolding. We know that it was Hazel Nut who was in Place 1. Therefore, it must have been her who used the cardboard scaffolding.

Elf	Place in photo	Accident	Quick fix
Candy Cane	3		
Cherry Pie	2		Hiding behind presents
Hazel Nut	1	Wonky walls	Cardboard scaffolding
Justin Thyme	5	Roof fell down	Super glue
Maple Syrup	4	Burnt pieces	2D house

I. We know that Cherry Pie's quick fix was hiding behind presents, Hazel Nut's quick fix was cardboard scaffolding, Justin Thyme's quick fix was super glue, and Maple Syrup's quick fix was turning her 3D house into a 2D house. It follows from this that Candy Cane's quick fix must have been a plastic dinosaur. We established in Explanation D that the gingerbread house whose quick fix was a plastic dinosaur had collapsed. Therefore, it was Candy Cane whose house collapsed and who fixed the situation with a plastic dinosaur.

We know that Candy Cane's house collapsed, Hazel Nut's house had wonky walls, Justin Thyme's house's roof fell down, and Maple Syrup burnt her gingerbread house's pieces. It follows from this that it must have been Cherry Pie whose decorations the reindeer licked off.

Elf	Place in photo	Accident	Quick fix
Candy Cane	3	Collapsed house	Plastic dinosaur
Cherry Pie	2	Reindeer licked off decorations	Hiding behind presents
Hazel Nut	1	Wonky walls	Cardboard scaffolding
Justin Thyme	5	Roof fell down	Super glue
Maple Syrup	4	Burnt pieces	2D house

4. Sweater You Like It or Not, I'm Wearing It!

A. Clue 6 indicates that the number of Woolverines' members was 1 fewer than another club's membership. This means that Woolverines cannot have had 8 members (i.e. the highest number of members).

Clue 7 states that the sweater *Time to Spruce Things Up!* was created by a club that had 1 more member than In Stitches and 2 fewer members than Woolverines. We established above that Woolverines' membership cannot have been 8. Therefore, the only way Clue 7 is true is if Woolverines had 7 members, the creators of *Time to Spruce Things Up!* had 5 members, and In Stitches had 4 members.

Design: Time to Spruce Things Up! = How many: 5

Knitting club	Design	How many	Unusual detail
Black Sheep			
In Stitches		4	
Knit Me Baby One More Time			
Pins & Needles			
Woolverines		7	

B. Clue 5 states that the combined number of members in Knit Me Baby One More Time and In Stitches was 12. We know that In Stitches had 4 members. Therefore, Knit Me Baby One More Time must have had 8 members.

Knitting club	Design	How many	Unusual detail
Black Sheep			
In Stitches		4	
Knit Me Baby One More Time		8	
Pins & Needles			
Woolverines		7	

C. Clue 3 indicates that the creators of *All Good Things Come in Trees* had 2 fewer members than Black Sheep. We know that In Stitches had 4 members, Knit Me Baby One More Time had 8 members, and Woolverines had

7 members. Therefore, Black Sheep must have had either 5 or 6 members. For the creators of *All Good Things Come in Trees* to have 2 fewer members than Black Sheep, Black Sheep must have had 6 members and the creators of *All Good Things Come in Trees* must have had 4 members.

We know that In Stitches had 4 members and we have now established that the creators of *All Good Things Come in Trees* had 4 members. Therefore, *All Good Things Come in Trees* must have been the design of In Stitches.

We know that Black Sheep had 6 members, In Stitches had 4 members, Knit Me Baby One More Time had 8 members, and Woolverines had 7 members. Therefore, Pins & Needles must have had 5 members.

Knitting club	Design	How many	Unusual detail
Black Sheep		6	
In Stitches	*All Good Things Come in Trees*	4	
Knit Me Baby One More Time		8	
Pins & Needles		5	
Woolverines		7	

D. We established in Explanation A that the number of members in the knitting club that designed *Time to Spruce Things Up!* was 5. We now know that Pins & Needles had 5 members. Therefore, *Time to Spruce Things Up!* was Pins & Needles' design.

Knitting club	Design	How many	Unusual detail
Black Sheep		6	
In Stitches	*All Good Things Come in Trees*	4	
Knit Me Baby One More Time		8	
Pins & Needles	*Time to Spruce Things Up!*	5	
Woolverines		7	

E. Clue 2 indicates that Pins & Needles' design included detachable Christmas goggles.

Clue 3 indicates that *All Good Things Come in Trees* included a button sounding a warning. We know that *All Good Things Come in Trees* was In Stitches' design. Therefore, it was In Stitches that included a warning button in their design.

Knitting club	Design	How many	Unusual detail
Black Sheep		6	
In Stitches	*All Good Things Come in Trees*	4	Warning button
Knit Me Baby One More Time		8	
Pins & Needles	*Time to Spruce Things Up!*	5	Detachable Christmas goggles
Woolverines		7	

F. Clue 6 indicates that the number of Woolverines' members was 1 fewer than the club whose jumper included skis in sleeves. We know that Woolverines' membership was 7. Therefore, the club whose jumper included skis in sleeves must have had a membership of 8. We know that Knit Me Baby One More Time had 8 members. Therefore, it must have been Knit Me Baby One More Time whose unusual design detail was skis in sleeves.

Knitting club	Design	How many	Unusual detail
Black Sheep		6	
In Stitches	*All Good Things Come in Trees*	4	Warning button
Knit Me Baby One More Time		8	Skis in sleeves
Pins & Needles	*Time to Spruce Things Up!*	5	Detachable Christmas goggles
Woolverines		7	

G. Clue 1 explains that there were 3 knitting clubs that called their creations jumpers and 2 knitting clubs that called them sweaters. Clue 3 indicates that *All Good Things Come in Trees* was created by a club that called them sweaters and Clue 7 indicates that *Time to Spruce Things Up!* was also called a sweater by their club members. We know that these 2 designs were created by In Stitches and Pins & Needles respectively. Therefore, the 3 remaining clubs – that is, Black Sheep, Knit Me Baby One More Time, and Woolverines – called their creations jumpers.

Clue 1 states that of the clubs that called their knitted garments jumpers, it was the 2nd in alphabetical order that had designed *Sleigh-ing It*. Now that we know that Black Sheep, Knit Me Baby One More Time, and Woolverines called their knitted garments jumpers, we can see that Knit Me Baby One More Time was the 2nd of these 3 clubs in alphabetical order. Therefore, *Sleigh-ing It* was designed by Knit Me Baby One More Time.

Knitting club	Design	How many	Unusual detail
Black Sheep		6	
In Stitches	*All Good Things Come in Trees*	4	Warning button
Knit Me Baby One More Time	*Sleigh-ing It*	8	Skis in sleeves
Pins & Needles	*Time to Spruce Things Up!*	5	Detachable Christmas goggles
Woolverines		7	

H. Clue 1 indicates that the club that designed *Sleigh-ing It* had 1 more member than the club whose design included a pop-up Christmas tree. We know that *Sleigh-ing It* was designed by Knit Me Baby One More Time and they had 8 members. Therefore, the club whose design included a pop-up Christmas tree must have had 7 members. We know that Woolverines had 7 members. Hence, Woolverines' design included a pop-up Christmas tree.

We know that In Stitches' design included a warning button, Knit Me Baby One More Time's design included skis in sleeves, Pins & Needles' design included detachable Christmas goggles, and Woolverines' design included a pop-up Christmas tree. It follows from this that Black Sheep's design must have included a kangaroo pouch.

Knitting club	Design	How many	Unusual detail
Black Sheep		6	Kangaroo pouch
In Stitches	*All Good Things Come in Trees*	4	Warning button
Knit Me Baby One More Time	*Sleigh-ing It*	8	Skis in sleeves
Pins & Needles	*Time to Spruce Things Up!*	5	Detachable Christmas goggles
Woolverines		7	Pop-up Christmas tree

I. Clue 4 states that the club whose jumpers incorporated kangaroo pouches had 1 fewer member than the club that created *Too Cool For Yule*. We know that Black Sheep's design included kangaroo pouches and they had 6 members. Therefore, the club that designed *Too Cool for Yule* must have had 7 members. We know that Woolverines had 7 members. Hence, it must have been Woolverines who designed *Too Cool for Yule*.

We know that In Stitches designed *All Good Things Come in Trees*, Knit Me Baby One More Time designed *Sleigh-ing It,* Pins & Needles designed *Time to Spruce Things Up!,* and Woolverines designed *Too Cool for Yule.* Therefore, it must be Black Sheep who designed *Hairy Christmas*.

Knitting club	Design	How many	Unusual detail
Black Sheep	*Hairy Christmas*	6	Kangaroo pouch
In Stitches	*All Good Things Come in Trees*	4	Warning button
Knit Me Baby One More Time	*Sleigh-ing It*	8	Skis in sleeves
Pins & Needles	*Time to Spruce Things Up!*	5	Detachable Christmas goggles
Woolverines	*Too Cool for Yule*	7	Pop-up Christmas tree

5. There's Snow Place Like Home

A. Clue 3 states that Frosty Fern's cousin's team built a castle that had no door. Clue 4 indicates that the captain of Rooftop Rebels was Crystal Clear's uncle and the dad of triplets. Apart from Breeze Block, Clue 3 does not state the names of the triplets. However, we can deduce that Crystal Clear must be the cousin of these triplets since there are 5 elves altogether in this puzzle: a dad (the Captain of Rooftop Rebels), his 3 offspring, and 1 other elf – i.e. the triplets' cousin Crystal Clear. Therefore, it is Crystal Clear's team whose snow castle had no door. Since it was Frosty Fern's cousin's team that built a castle that had no door, we can also conclude that Frosty Fern must be 1 of the triplets along with Breeze Block.

Rooftop Rebel's captain = Crystal Clear's uncle = Breeze Block and Frosty Fern's dad

Captain	Area	Team	Problem
Breeze Block			
Crystal Clear			No door
Frosty Fern			
North Pole			
Snow Lily			

B. We established in Explanation A that the captain of Rooftop Rebels was Crystal Clear's uncle, and Breeze Block and Frosty Fern's dad. Therefore, the name of Rooftop Rebels' captain cannot be Crystal Clear, Breeze Block, or Frosty Fern. Clue 2 indicates that Snow Lily is female as it mentions her team's area. Therefore, Rooftop Rebels' captain cannot be Snow Lily. It follows from this that North Pole has to be Rooftop Rebels' captain. We can now also deduce that Snow Lily must be North Pole's daughter and 1 of the triplets.

North Pole = Crystal Clear's uncle = Breeze Block, Frosty Fern, and Snow Lily's dad

Captain	Area	Team	Problem
Breeze Block			
Crystal Clear			No door
Frosty Fern			
North Pole		Rooftop Rebels	
Snow Lily			

C. Clue 1 indicates that the snow castle that was built in Area 5 was too small.

Area: 5 = Problem: Too small

D. Clue 4 states that Rooftop Rebels' captain was the dad of triplets: Breeze Block, the captain of the team whose castle was too small, and the captain of Snow Angels. We established in Explanation B that Rooftop Rebels' captain was called North Pole and his offspring were called Breeze Block, Frosty Fern, and Snow Lily. When we combine these pieces of information, we can deduce that Frosty Fern and Snow Lily, one's team built a castle that was too small and the other was the captain of Snow Angels (but not necessarily in this order). Let's first focus on Snow Lily and figure out whether her team's castle was too small or whether she was the captain of Snow Angels.

Clue 2 states that Snow Lily's team's area was farther north than Not So Great Expectations' area. When we look at the diagram, we can deduce that Snow Lily's area cannot have been Area 5 as that area is farthest south. We established in Explanation C that the castle built in Area 5 was too small. It follows from this that Snow Lily's castle cannot have been the one that was too small. Therefore, Snow Lily must have been the captain of Snow Angels. It follows from this that Frosty Fern must have been the captain of the team whose castle was too small, which, as we know from Explanation C, was located in Area 5.

Captain	Area	Team	Problem
Breeze Block			
Crystal Clear			No door
Frosty Fern	5		Too small
North Pole		Rooftop Rebels	
Snow Lily		Snow Angels	

E. Clue 3 indicates that there was an area that touched the west side of North Pole's team's area while also touching the northwest side of Crystal Clear's team's area. When we look at the diagram, we can see that Areas 1, 2, 3, and 4 touched each other in different ways (Area 5 was separate from the other areas). For this area to touch simultaneously the west side of North Pole's team's area and the northwest side Crystal Clear's team's area, this area had to be Area 1, North Pole's team's area had to be Area 2, and Crystal Clear's team's area had to be Area 4.

Clue 3 further indicates that this area in question – which we now know was Area 1 – had a castle that had a hole in the wall.

Area: 1 = Problem = Hole in the wall

Captain	Area	Team	Problem
Breeze Block			
Crystal Clear	4		No door
Frosty Fern	5		Too small
North Pole	2	Rooftop Rebels	
Snow Lily		Snow Angels	

F. We now know that Crystal Clear's team was in Area 4, Frosty Fern's team was in Area 5, and North Pole's team was in Area 2. It follows from this that of Breeze Block and Snow Lily, one's team was in Area 1 and the other's team was in Area 3 (but not necessarily in this order). Clue 4 indicates that the area number of the Snow Angels was higher than the area number of its captain's dad's team. We know from Explanations B and D that the captain of Snow Angels was Snow Lily and her dad was North Pole. This means that we can reformulate the clue as follows: Snow Lily's team's area number was higher than North Pole's team's area number. We know that North Pole's team's area number was 2. Therefore, of the area numbers that are still unsolved – that is, Areas 1 and 3 – Snow Lily's team's area number must have been Area 3. It follows from this that Breeze Block's team must have been in Area 1.

Captain	Area	Team	Problem
Breeze Block	1		
Crystal Clear	4		No door
Frosty Fern	5		Too small
North Pole	2	Rooftop Rebels	
Snow Lily	3	Snow Angels	

G. We established in Explanation E that the snow castle with a hole in the wall was positioned in Area 1. We now know that Breeze Block's team was in Area 1. Therefore, it was Breeze Block's team that built a snow castle that ended up with a hole in the wall.

Captain	Area	Team	Problem
Breeze Block	1		Hole in the wall
Crystal Clear	4		No door
Frosty Fern	5		Too small
North Pole	2	Rooftop Rebels	
Snow Lily	3	Snow Angels	

H. Clue 5 indicates that the odd-shaped snow castle was located east of the one that had a collapsed roof. We know that the castle in Area 1 had a hole in the wall, the castle in Area 4 had no door, and the castle in Area 5 was too small. Therefore, the odd-shaped castle and the castle with a collapsed roof must have been located in Areas 2 and 3 (but not necessarily in that order). Since Area 3 is located east of Area 2, the odd-shaped castle must have been in Area 3 and the castle with a collapsed roof must have been in Area 2.

Captain	Area	Team	Problem
Breeze Block	1		Hole in the wall
Crystal Clear	4		No door
Frosty Fern	5		Too small
North Pole	2	Rooftop Rebels	Roof collapsed
Snow Lily	3	Snow Angels	Odd shape

I. Clue 4 states that Rooftop Rebels' area was not adjacent to Fa La La Family's area. We know that Rooftop Rebels' area was Area 2. When we look at the diagram, the only area that is not adjacent to this area is Area 5.

Therefore, Fa La La Family's area must be Area 5. We know that Frosty Fern's team was in Area 5, so it is Frosty Fern whose team was called Fa La La Family.

Captain	Area	Team	Problem
Breeze Block	1		Hole in the wall
Crystal Clear	4		No door
Frosty Fern	5	Fa La La Family	Too small
North Pole	2	Rooftop Rebels	Roof collapsed
Snow Lily	3	Snow Angels	Odd shape

J. Clue 2 states that Snow Lily's team's area was farther north from the area where Not So Great Expectations built their castle and that her team's area did not touch the Parumpapapums' area. We know that Snow Lily's team was in Area 3. We also know that Rooftop Rebels captained by North Pole were in Area 2 and Fa La La Family captained by Frosty Fern were in Area 5. This leaves Areas 1 and 4 as possible areas for Not So Great Expectations and The Parumpapapums (but not necessarily in this order). For Snow Lily's team's Area 3 to be farther north from Not So Great Expectations' area and not touch The Parumpapapums' area, the team of Not So Great Expectations must have been in Area 4 and The Papumpapapums must have been in Area 1. We know that Crystal Clear's team was in Area 4 and Breeze Block's team was in Area 1. It follows from this that Crystal Clear's team must have been called Not So Great Expectations and Breeze Block's team must have been called The Parumpapapums.

Captain	Area	Team	Problem
Breeze Block	1	The Parumpapapums	Hole in the wall
Crystal Clear	4	Not So Great Expectations	No door
Frosty Fern	5	Fa La La Family	Too small
North Pole	2	Rooftop Rebels	Roof collapsed
Snow Lily	3	Snow Angels	Odd shape

6. Elf Portrait

A. Clue 1 indicates that Elfred Einstein had grown a beard because he had forgotten to shave.

Elf	Place in photo	Why beard	Combing time
Billy Elfiot			
Elfis Presley			
Elfon John			
Elfred Einstein		Forgot to shave	
Elf Sheeran			

B. Clue 4 indicates that 3 of Cam Era's best friends were accomplished singers and were lead vocalists. They were positioned in front of the elf crowd and were near the bottom edge of the photo. When we look at the picture, we can see that these were the elves in Places 3, 4, and 5.

Clue 3 indicates the Elfis Presley was a singer. Clues 6 and 7 indicate that Elfon John was a singer. Clue 8 indicates that Elf Sheeran was a singer and stood in front of the elf crowd next to another elf. Since we established above that the singer elves were in Places 3, 4, and 5, we can deduce that Elfis Presley, Elfon John, and Elf Sheeran must have been in Places 3, 4, and 5 (but not necessarily in this order). Furthermore, since Elf Sheeran was positioned in front of the elf crowd next to another elf, he must have been either in Place 3 or 5.

Since Elfis Presley, Elfon John, and Elf Sheeran were in Places 3, 4, and 5 (but not necessarily in this order), it follows from this that Billy Elfiot and Elfred Einstein must have been in Places 1 and 2 (but not necessarily in this order).

Elf: Billy Elfiot = Place in photo: 1 OR 2
Elf: Elfis Presley = Place in photo: 3 OR 4 OR 5
Elf: Elfon John = Place in photo: 3 OR 4 OR 5
Elf: Elfred Einstein = Place in photo: 1 OR 2
Elf: Elf Sheeran = Place in photo: 3 OR 5

C. Clue 5 states that the elf who had grown a beard in order to keep his face warm had the shortest beard-combing time. In other words, this elf spent 1 min combing his beard in the mornings.

Clue 4 indicates that none of Cam Era's singer friends were as quick to comb their beards in the mornings as the elf in Place 1. This is to say that none of Cam Era's singer friends spent the least amount of time – that is, 1 min – combing their beards in the morning. We established in Explanation B that Cam Era's singer friends were Elfis Presley, Elfon John, and Elf Sheeran. Therefore, it must have been either Billy Elfiot or Elfred Einstein who spent 1 min combing his beard in the mornings.

Since Clue 5 states that the elf who had grown a beard in order to keep his face warm had the shortest beard-combing time, and since we know that Elfred Einstein had grown a beard because he had initially forgotten to shave, he cannot be the one who had grown a beard in order to keep his face warm. It follows from this that it must have been Billy Elfiot who had grown a beard in order to keep his face warm and had the shortest beard-combing time of 1 min.

Elf	Place in photo	Why beard	Combing time
Billy Elfiot		Keeps face warm	1 min
Elfis Presley			
Elfon John			
Elfred Einstein		Forgot to shave	
Elf Sheeran			

D. Clue 6 indicates that 1 of the 3 lead vocalists spent 1 min less time grooming his beard than the elf in Place 2. We established in Explanation B that Billy Elfiot and Elfred Einstein were in Places 1 and 2. Therefore, we can express the information in Clue 6 as follows: 1 of the 3 lead vocalists spent 1 min less time grooming his beard than either Billy Elfiot or Elfred Einstein. We know that Billy Elfiot spent 1 min, which is the least amount of time, grooming his beard. Hence, it is not possible that another elf could spent less time grooming his beard. It follows from this that it must have been Elfred Einstein who was in Place 2 and whose grooming time was compared to the grooming time of 1 of the 3 lead vocalists.

We established in Explanation B that Billy Elfiot was either in Place 1 or 2. We now know that Elfred Einstein was in Place 2. Therefore, Billy Elfiot must have been in Place 1.

Elf	Place in photo	Why beard	Combing time
Billy Elfiot	1	Keeps face warm	1 min
Elfis Presley			
Elfon John			
Elfred Einstein	2	Forgot to shave	
Elf Sheeran			

E. Clue 7 indicates that Elfon John's beard took 3 mins longer to comb than the beard of the elf in Place 2. We know that the elf in Place 2 was Elfred Einstein. Since Billy Elfiot's combing time was 1 min, the remaining combing time options leave only 1 combination that is possible: Elfon John's combing time must have been 7 mins and Elfred Einstein's combing time must have been 4 mins.

Elf	Place in photo	Why beard	Combing time
Billy Elfiot	1	Keeps face warm	1 min
Elfis Presley			
Elfon John			7 mins
Elfred Einstein	2	Forgot to shave	4 mins
Elf Sheeran			

F. We know that Billy Elfiot in Place 1 spent 1 min combing his beard, Elfon John spent 7 mins combing his beard, and Elfred Einstein in Place 2 spent 4 mins combing his beard. Therefore, of Elfis Presley and Elf Sheeran, one spent 3 mins and the other 5 mins combing their beards (but not necessarily in this order).

Clue 3 states that the combined beard combing time of the elves in Places 1 and 3 was less than how long Elfis Presley spent combing his beard. We know that the elf in Place 1 – Billy Elfiot – spent 1 min combing his beard. We also established above that Elfis Presley spent either 3 mins or 5 mins combing his beard. Let's see which option might be true: If Elfis Presley spent 3 mins combing his beard, the elves in Places 1 and 3 would both have to have spent 1 min combing their beards for the sum of their combing time to be less than 3 mins. Since the combing time options won't allow 2 elves to have the same combing time of 1 min, we can deduce that Elfis Presley's combing time cannot have been 3 mins, and hence, it must have been 5 mins.

60

We now know that Elfis Presley's combing time was 5 mins and the combing time of the elf in Place 1 was 1 min. Therefore, the combing time of the elf in Place 3 must have been 3 mins (so that the sum of the combing time of the elves in Places 1 and 3 is under 5 mins). We know that Billy Elfiot's combing time was 1 min, Elfis Presley's combing time was 5 mins, Elfon John's combing time was 7 mins, and Elfred Einstein's combing time was 4 mins. It follows from this that Elf Sheeran's combing time must have been 3 mins. Since we know that the elf who spent 3 mins combing his beard was in Place 3, we can deduce that this elf must have been Elf Sheeran.

Elf	Place in photo	Why beard	Combing time
Billy Elfiot	1	Keeps face warm	1 min
Elfis Presley			5 mins
Elfon John			7 mins
Elfred Einstein	2	Forgot to shave	4 mins
Elf Sheeran	3		3 mins

G. Clue 2 states that the elf who used his beard to keep his hands warm spent 2 mins longer combing his beard than the elf in Place 4. We know that Billy Elfiot was in Place 1, Elfred Einstein was in Place 2, and Elf Sheeran was in Place 3. Therefore, it was either Elfis Presley or Elfon John who was in Place 4. Elfis Presley's combing time was 5 mins and Elfon John's combing time was 7 mins.

As mentioned above, Clue 2 states that the elf who used his beard to keep his hands warm spent 2 mins longer combing his beard than the elf in Place 4. This is to say that the elf in Place 4 cannot have had the longest combing time of 7 mins, as the elf who used his beard to keep his hands warm spent 2 mins longer doing the task. Since Elfon John spent 7 mins combing his beard, he cannot have been in Place 4. It follows from this that it must have been Elfis Presley who was in Place 4.

Since Billy Elfiot was in Place 1, Elfis Presley in Place 4, Elfred Einstein in Place 2, and Elf Sheeran in Place 3, it must have been Elfon John who was in Place 5.

Elf	Place in photo	Why beard	Combing time
Billy Elfiot	1	Keeps face warm	1 min
Elfis Presley	4		5 mins
Elfon John	5		7 mins
Elfred Einstein	2	Forgot to shave	4 mins
Elf Sheeran	3		3 mins

H. Clue 2 states that the elf who used his beard to keep his hands warm spent 2 mins longer combing his beard than the elf in Place 4. We know that the elf in Place 4 was Elfis Presley and he spent 5 mins combing his beard. Therefore, the elf who used his beard to keep his hands warm and who spent 2 mins longer combing his beard must have spent 7 mins doing this task. We know that it was Elfon John who spent 7 mins combing his beard. Therefore, it must be him who used his beard to keep his hands warm.

Elf	Place in photo	Why beard	Combing time
Billy Elfiot	1	Keeps face warm	1 min
Elfis Presley	4		5 mins
Elfon John	5	Keeps hands warm	7 mins
Elfred Einstein	2	Forgot to shave	4 mins
Elf Sheeran	3		3 mins

I. Clue 6 indicates that of the 3 lead vocalist elves, one had grown a beard because he had lost a dare, another was called Elfon John, and the 3rd one spent 1 min less time grooming than the elf in Place 2. We established in Explanation B that the singer elves who also occupied lead vocalist roles were Elfis Presley, Elfon John, and Elf Sheeran. Since Clue 6 identifies Elfon John as one of the lead vocalists, we can deduce that it refers to Elfis Presley and Elf Sheeran when it mentions the elf who had grown a beard because he had lost a dare and the elf who spent 1 min less time grooming than the elf in Place 2. We know that the elf in Place 2 was Elfred Einstein and he spent 4 mins combing his beard. The elf who spent 1 min less – i.e. 3 mins – was Elf Sheeran. Therefore, the elf who had grown a beard because he had lost a dare must have been Elfis Presley.

We now know that Billy Elfiot grew a beard to keep his face warm, Elfis Presley grew a beard because he lost a dare, Elfon John grew a beard to keep his hands warm, and Elfred Einstein grew a beard because he initially

forgot to shave. It follows from this that Elf Sheeran must have grown a beard because he thought it looked Christmassy.

Elf	Place in photo	Why beard	Combing time
Billy Elfiot	1	Keeps face warm	1 min
Elfis Presley	4	Lost a dare	5 mins
Elfon John	5	Keeps hands warm	7 mins
Elfred Einstein	2	Forgot to shave	4 mins
Elf Sheeran	3	Looks Christmassy	3 mins

7. Behind Claused Doors

A. Clue 11 states that Elf Dorado found the last map. Clue 4 states that the elf who found the last map took it out from the middle shelf. This is to say that Elf Dorado must have taken the map from the middle shelf. When we look at the picture, we can see that the middle shelf is Shelf 3. Therefore, Elf Dorado found a map on Shelf 3.

Elf	Map	Shelf	Next to book
Britney Steers			
Elf Dorado		3	
Harry Caine			
Joy Ride			
Max Speed			

B. Clue 8 indicates that Max Speed found a map on a shelf that had black folders. When we look at the picture, we can see that Shelves 2 and 3 have black folders. Since we know that Elf Dorado found a map on Shelf 3, Max Speed must have found a map on Shelf 2.

Elf	Map	Shelf	Next to book
Britney Steers			
Elf Dorado		3	
Harry Caine			
Joy Ride			
Max Speed		2	

C. Clue 1 states that Britney Steers found a map on a higher shelf than Elf Dorado. We know that Elf Dorado found a map on Shelf 3. We also know that Max Speed found a map on Shelf 2, and therefore, Britney Steers couldn't have found a map on Shelf 2. It follows from this that she must have found a map on Shelf 1.

Elf	Map	Shelf	Next to book
Britney Steers		1	
Elf Dorado		3	
Harry Caine			
Joy Ride			
Max Speed		2	

D. Clue 6 indicates that the genetic map was found next to Rudolph's favorite book *Fifty Shades of Sleigh* and that the elf who found it had the letter E in her last name. In other words, it was a female elf who found the genetic map next to *Fifty Shades of Sleigh*.

Clue 7 indicates that Harry Caine was male, Clue 8 indicates that Max Speed was male, and Clue 11 indicates that Elf Dorado was male. Therefore, none of them could have found the genetic map next to *Fifty Shades of Sleigh*. Clue 9 indicates that Joy Ride didn't find a map on a shelf that had Rudolph's favorite book on it – which we know was *Fifty Shades of Sleigh*. This means that Joy Ride cannot have found the genetic map next to *Fifty Shades of Sleigh*. It follows from this that it must have been Britney Steers who found the genetic map next to *Fifty Shades of Sleigh*.

Elf	Map	Shelf	Next to book
Britney Steers	Genetic map	1	*Fifty Shades of Sleigh*
Elf Dorado		3	
Harry Caine			
Joy Ride			
Max Speed		2	

E. Clue 10 states that *Alice in Winter Wonderland* was on a shelf that had black folders on it. When we look at the picture, we can see that there are black folders on Shelves 2 and 3. Therefore, *Alice in Winter Wonderland* must have been on Shelf 2 or 3.

Clue 7 indicates that the fate map was on a shelf right above *Alice in Winter Wonderland*. Since *Alice in Winter Wonderland* was on Shelf 2 or 3, the fate must have been on Shelf 1 or 2 respectively. We know that the genetic map was on Shelf 1. Therefore, the fate map must have been on Shelf 2 and *Alice in Winter Wonderland* must have been on Shelf 3.

We know that Max Speed found a map on Shelf 2. Therefore, he must have found the fate map. We also know that Elf Dorado found a map on Shelf 3. Hence, he must have found it next to *Alice in Winter Wonderland*.

Elf	Map	Shelf	Next to book
Britney Steers	Genetic map	1	*Fifty Shades of Sleigh*
Elf Dorado		3	*Alice in Winter Wonderland*
Harry Caine			
Joy Ride			
Max Speed	Fate map	2	

F. Clue 9 indicates that the heat map and the inclusion map were not on a shelf where Joy Ride found a map. This is to say, Joy Ride found neither the heat map nor the inclusion map. We also know that it was Britney Steers who found the genetic map and Max Speed who found the fate map. It follows from this that Joy Ride must have found the mind map.

Elf	Map	Shelf	Next to book
Britney Steers	Genetic map	1	*Fifty Shades of Sleigh*
Elf Dorado		3	*Alice in Winter Wonderland*
Harry Caine			
Joy Ride	Mind map		
Max Speed	Fate map	2	

G. Clue 3 indicates that the mind map was found 2 shelves lower than *Noel Country for Old Men* and that the higher of these shelves had black folders on it. Since it is the shelf where *Noel Country for Old Men* was that was the higher of these 2 shelves, we can deduce that *Noel Country for Old Men* must have been on a shelf that had black folders on it. When we look at the picture, we can see that the black folders are on Shelves 2 and 3. However, we know that *Alice in Winter Wonderland* was on Shelf 3. Therefore, *Noel Country for Old Men* must have been on Shelf 2 – which we know was the shelf where Max Speed found a map.

Since Clue 3 indicates that the mind map was 2 shelves lower than *Noel Country for Old Men*, and we have now established that *Noel Country for Old Men* was on Shelf 2, the mind map must have been on Shelf 4. We know that Joy Ride found the mind map. Hence, she must have found it on Shelf 4.

We know that Britney Steers found a map on Shelf 1, Elf Dorado found a map on Shelf 3, Joy Ride found a map on Shelf 4, and Max Speed found a map on Shelf 2. Therefore, it must be Harry Caine who found a map on Shelf 5.

Elf	Map	Shelf	Next to book
Britney Steers	Genetic map	1	*Fifty Shades of Sleigh*
Elf Dorado		3	*Alice in Winter Wonderland*
Harry Caine		5	
Joy Ride	Mind map	4	
Max Speed	Fate map	2	*Noel Country for Old Men*

H. Clue 2 indicates that *The Jingle Bell Jar* was on a higher shelf than the inclusion map. We know that *Fifty Shades of Sleigh* was on Shelf 1, *Alice in Winter Wonderland* was on Shelf 3, and *Noel Country for Old Men* was on Shelf 2. Therefore, *The Jingle Bell Jar* must have been on either Shelf 4 or Shelf 5. Since it was on a higher shelf than the inclusion map, it must have been on Shelf 4 and, consequently, the inclusion map must have been on Shelf 5. We know that Joy Ride found a map on Shelf 4. Therefore, she must have found it next to *The Jingle Bell Jar*. We also know that Harry Caine found a map on Shelf 5. Hence, he must have found the inclusion map.

Elf	Map	Shelf	Next to book
Britney Steers	Genetic map	1	*Fifty Shades of Sleigh*
Elf Dorado		3	*Alice in Winter Wonderland*
Harry Caine	Inclusion map	5	
Joy Ride	Mind map	4	*The Jingle Bell Jar*
Max Speed	Fate map	2	*Noel Country for Old Men*

I. We know that Britney Steers found the genetic map, Harry Caine found the inclusion map, Joy Ride found the mind map, and Max Speed found the fate map. Therefore, it must have been Elf Dorado who found the heat map.

We know that Britney Steers found a map next to *Fifty Shades of Sleigh*, Elf Dorado found a map next to *Alice in Winter Wonderland*, Joy Ride found a map next to *The Jingle Bell Jar*, and Max Speed found a map next to *Noel Country for Old Men*. Therefore, it must have been Harry Caine who found a map next to *Frankincense and Sensibility*.

Elf	Map	Shelf	Next to book
Britney Steers	Genetic map	1	*Fifty Shades of Sleigh*
Elf Dorado	Heat map	3	*Alice in Winter Wonderland*
Harry Caine	Inclusion map	5	*Frankincense and Sensibility*
Joy Ride	Mind map	4	*The Jingle Bell Jar*
Max Speed	Fate map	2	*Noel Country for Old Men*

8. Candy Canes in Mint Condition

A. Clue 1 states that Angel Cake used red and green colors in her candy canes even though neither color really depicted her chosen flavors, unless the tenuous link to green pumpkin stems was considered to be part of her decision-making process. This indicates that there was a pumpkin flavor in Angel Cake's candy canes. When we look at the flavor options, we can see that the only option that includes pumpkin is a pumpkin pie & cinnamon flavor. Therefore, we can deduce that Angel Cake's chosen flavor was pumpkin pie & cinnamon.

Elf	Flavor	Display title	How many
Angel Cake	Pumpkin pie & cinnamon		
Basil Oil			
Cedar Apple			
Devon Cream			
Ginger Bread			

B. Clue 4 states that Ginger Bread's artwork consisted of over 10 more candy canes than *Twelve Sprays of Christmas*. When we look at the options in the 'How many' section in the grid, we can deduce that Ginger Bread's artwork must have consisted of 75 candy canes and *Twelve Sprays of Christmas* must have consisted of 60 or 63 candy canes.

Display title: Twelve Sprays of Christmas = How many: 60 OR 63

Elf	Flavor	Display title	How many
Angel Cake	Pumpkin pie & cinnamon		
Basil Oil			
Cedar Apple			
Devon Cream			
Ginger Bread			75

C. Clue 3 tells us that *Twelve Sleighs of Christmas* depicted 34 sleighs and that each sleigh had a pair of candy canes as its runners. This is to say that each of the 34 sleighs included 2 candy canes. To get the total number of candy canes in the display, we need to multiply 34 by 2. This equals 68. This is to say that *Twelve Sleighs of Christmas* consisted of 68 candy canes.

Display title: Twelve Sleighs of Christmas = How many: 68

D. We know that Ginger Bread's artwork consisted of 75 candy canes. We established in Explanation B that *Twelve Sprays of Christmas* consisted of either 60 or 63 candy canes. Therefore, Ginger Bread's artwork cannot have been *Twelve Sprays of Christmas*. We also established in Explanation C that *Twelve Sleighs of Christmas* had 68 candy canes. Hence, Ginger Bread's display cannot have been *Twelve Sleighs of Christmas*. Clue 5 indicates that *Twelve Ways of Christmas* had fewer than 70 candy canes. This means that *Twelve Ways of Christmas* cannot have been Ginger Bread's artwork. Furthermore, in Clue 8 Ginger Bread's candy canes are compared to the canes in *Twelve Plays of Christmas*. Therefore, Ginger Bread's display cannot have been called *Twelve Plays of Christmas*. It follows from this that Ginger Bread's display must have been called *Twelve Trays of Christmas*.

Elf	Flavor	Display title	How many
Angel Cake	Pumpkin pie & cinnamon		
Basil Oil			
Cedar Apple			
Devon Cream			
Ginger Bread		*Twelve Trays of Christmas*	75

E. Clue 5 indicates that *Twelve Ways of Christmas* had fewer than 70 candy canes. We established in Explanation C that *Twelve Sleighs of Christmas* had 68 candy canes. Therefore, *Twelve Ways of Christmas* must have had either 60 or 63 canes.

We established above and in Explanation B that *Twelve Ways of Christmas* and *Twelve Sprays of Christmas* had 60 and 63 candy canes (but not necessarily in this order). We also know that Ginger Bread's *Twelve Trays of Christmas* had 75 canes. Furthermore, we established in Explanation C that *Twelve Sleighs of Christmas* had 68 canes. Therefore, *Twelve Plays of Christmas* must have had 70 canes.

Display title: Twelve Ways of Christmas = How many: 60 OR 63
Display title: Twelve Plays of Christmas = How many: 70

F. Clue 2 states that the combined number of candy canes whose flavors included cinnamon was fewer than 130. When we look at the grid, we can see that there are 2 flavors that include cinnamon: apple pie & cinnamon and pumpkin pie & cinnamon. When we look at the options in the 'How many' section in the grid, we can deduce that there are only 2 combinations that keep the combined number of these candy canes below 130:

1. 60 canes + 63 canes = 123 canes
2. 60 canes + 68 canes = 128 canes

Therefore, the number of the apple pie & cinnamon canes or the pumpkin pie & cinnamon candy canes cannot have been 70 or 75.

We now know that the number of apple pie & cinnamon canes and the number of pumpkin pie & cinnamon canes were 60 and either 63 or 68, but we don't know yet in which combination. Clue 6 indicates that there was a display that had 3 fewer candy canes than the display made of coffee & caramel canes. When we look at the options in the grid, we can see that there is only 1 combination where this is possible: there had to be 63 coffee & caramel canes and 60 of the other canes. This is to say that of the apple pie & cinnamon canes and the pumpkin pie & cinnamon canes, neither display had 63 pieces. It follows from this that of the apple pie & cinnamon cane display and the pumpkin pie & cinnamon cane display, one had 60 canes in it and the other 68 canes (but not necessarily in this order).

Flavor: Pumpkin pie & cinnamon = How many: 60 OR 68
Flavor: Apple pie & cinnamon = How many: 60 OR 68
Flavor: Coffee & caramel = How many: 63

G. We know that Ginger Bread's display was called *Twelve Trays of Christmas*. Therefore, it cannot have been Angel Cake's display title. Clue 1 states that Angel Cake's candy canes were red and green, and Clue 5 states that *Twelve Ways of Christmas* consisted of yellow-and-white canes. Hence, *Twelve Ways of Christmas* cannot have been Angel Cake's display title. Clue 4 indicates that *Twelve Sprays of Christmas* did not have any pie-flavored candy canes. We know that Angel Cake's canes had the pumpkin pie & cinnamon flavor. Therefore, her display title cannot have been *Twelve Sprays of Christmas*. We established in Explanation E that *Twelve Plays of Christmas* had 70 canes and in Explanation F that the display that consisted of pumpkin pie & cinnamon flavored canes – which we know were Angel Cake's candy canes – had 60 or 68 canes. Hence, *Twelve Plays of Christmas* cannot have been Angel Cake's display. It follows from this that Angel

Cake's display must have been *Twelve Sleighs of Christmas*.

Elf	Flavor	Display title	How many
Angel Cake	Pumpkin pie & cinnamon	*Twelve Sleighs of Christmas*	
Basil Oil			
Cedar Apple			
Devon Cream			
Ginger Bread		*Twelve Trays of Christmas*	75

H. We established in Explanation C that *Twelve Sleighs of Christmas* consisted of 68 candy canes. Since Angel Cake's display was *Twelve Sleighs of Christmas*, it was her who made a display from 68 candy canes.

We established in Explanation F that the display consisting of apple pie & cinnamon flavored canes had either 60 or 68 canes. We now know that there were 68 pumpkin & cinnamon flavored canes in Angel Cake's display. Therefore, there must have been 60 apple pie & cinnamon flavored canes.

Flavor: Apple pie & cinnamon = How many: 60

Elf	Flavor	Display title	How many
Angel Cake	Pumpkin pie & cinnamon	*Twelve Sleighs of Christmas*	68
Basil Oil			
Cedar Apple			
Devon Cream			
Ginger Bread		*Twelve Trays of Christmas*	75

I. Clue 7 states that Basil Oil's display had more canes than either of the displays of his fellow elves whose 1st names had the letter A in them. The elves whose 1st names have the letter A in them (apart from Basil Oil himself) are: Angel Cake and Cedar Apple. We know that Angel Cake's display had 68 canes. Therefore, Basil Oil's display must have had more canes than that. Since Ginger Bread's display had 75 canes, Basil Oil's display must have had 70 canes.

We established in Explanation E that *Twelve Plays of Christmas* had 70 canes. Since we now know that Basil Oil's display consisted of 70 canes, we can deduce that Basil Oil must have named his display *Twelve Plays of Christmas*.

Elf	Flavor	Display title	How many
Angel Cake	Pumpkin pie & cinnamon	*Twelve Sleighs of Christmas*	68
Basil Oil		*Twelve Plays of Christmas*	70
Cedar Apple			
Devon Cream			
Ginger Bread		*Twelve Trays of Christmas*	75

J. Clue 6 states that of *Twelve Plays of Christmas* and Devon Cream's creation, one had vanilla in it and the other had 3 fewer canes that the display made of coffee & caramel canes. We established in Explanation F that there were 63 coffee & caramel canes. For there to be 3 fewer canes than the coffee & caramel canes, the number of these canes would have to be 60. We can now express Clue 6 as follows: Of *Twelve Plays of Christmas* and Devon Cream's creation, one had vanilla in it and the other had 60 canes. We know that *Twelve Plays of Christmas*, which was Basil Oil's creation, consisted of 70 canes. Therefore, it cannot have been the display with 60 canes and must, instead, have been the display whose canes were flavored with vanilla. When we look at the grid, we can see that the full flavor combination is blueberry pie & vanilla. This is to say that *Twelve Plays of Christmas* consisted of candy canes flavored with blueberry pie & vanilla. It follows from this that Devon Cream's display must have included 60 canes.

Since Angel Cake's display had 68 canes, Basil Oil's display had 70 canes, Devon Cream's display had 60 canes, and Ginger Bread's display had 75 canes, it must be Cedar Apple whose display consisted of 63 canes. We know from Explanation F that there were 63 coffee & caramel canes. Hence, Cedar Apple's display must have included 63 coffee & caramel canes.

Elf	Flavor	Display title	How many
Angel Cake	Pumpkin pie & cinnamon	*Twelve Sleighs of Christmas*	68
Basil Oil	Blueberry pie & vanilla	*Twelve Plays of Christmas*	70
Cedar Apple	Coffee & caramel		63
Devon Cream			60
Ginger Bread		*Twelve Trays of Christmas*	75

K. We established in Explanation H that there were 60 apple pie & cinnamon canes in a display. We know that Devon Cream used 60 candy canes. Therefore, Devon Cream's chosen flavor must have been apple pie & cinnamon.

Since Angel Cake's flavor was pumpkin pie & cinnamon, Basil Oil's flavor was blueberry pie & vanilla, Cedar Apple's flavor was coffee & caramel, and Devon Cream's flavor was apple pie & cinnamon, it must be Ginger Bread whose flavor was chocolate & mint.

Elf	Flavor	Display title	How many
Angel Cake	Pumpkin pie & cinnamon	*Twelve Sleighs of Christmas*	68
Basil Oil	Blueberry pie & vanilla	*Twelve Plays of Christmas*	70
Cedar Apple	Coffee & caramel		63
Devon Cream	Apple pie & cinnamon		60
Ginger Bread	Chocolate & mint	*Twelve Trays of Christmas*	75

L. Clue 4 indicates that *Twelve Sprays of Christmas* did not contain any pie-flavored candy canes. There are only 2 options where a pie flavor wasn't used: coffee & caramel and chocolate & mint. Since we know that Ginger Bread's *Twelve Trays of Christmas* consisted of chocolate & mint canes, *Twelve Sprays of Christmas* must have consisted of coffee & caramel canes – which we know was the flavor combination that Cedar Apple had chosen.

We know that Angel Cake's display was *Twelve Sleighs of Christmas*, Basil Oil's display was *Twelve Plays of Christmas*, Cedar Apple's display was *Twelve Sprays of Christmas*, and Ginger Bread's display was *Twelve Trays of Christmas*. Therefore, Devon Cream's display must have been *Twelve Ways of Christmas*.

Elf	Flavor	Display title	How many
Angel Cake	Pumpkin pie & cinnamon	*Twelve Sleighs of Christmas*	68
Basil Oil	Blueberry pie & vanilla	*Twelve Plays of Christmas*	70
Cedar Apple	Coffee & caramel	*Twelve Sprays of Christmas*	63
Devon Cream	Apple pie & cinnamon	*Twelve Ways of Christmas*	60
Ginger Bread	Chocolate & mint	*Twelve Trays of Christmas*	75

9. Holding on for Deer Life

A. Clue 5 indicates that Ryde Ansing's ski suit was red and Wunorse Openslae's ski suit was green. Clue 7 indicates that there were 2 male elves in yellow ski suits. Clue 4 indicates that Jingle Belle was female. Therefore, Dashin Throothesnoe and Owot Fun must have been male and must have been wearing yellow ski suits.

Dashin Throothesnoe = Yellow ski suit = Male
Jingle Belle = Ski suit color not known = Female
Owot Fun = Yellow ski suit = Male
Ryde Ansing = Red ski suit = Gender not yet known
Wunorse Openslae = Green ski suit = Gender not yet known

B. Clue 7 indicates that of the 2 male elves in yellow ski suits – whom we know from Explanation A were Dashin Throothesnoe and Owot Fun – one had poor steering and the other fell over (but not necessarily in this order).

Clue 3 indicates that Owot Fun came 1 place higher than the elf whose steering left much to be desired. This means that Owot Fun cannot have been the elf with poor steering and must have been the one who fell over. It follows from this that Dashin Throothesnoe must have been the one with poor steering.

Elf	Reindeer	Ranking	Slowed down by
Dashin Throothesnoe			Poor steering
Jingle Belle			
Owot Fun			Falling over
Ryde Ansing			
Wunorse Openslae			

C. Clue 2 states that Reinald Deere ended up in Rudolph's bootcamp. Clue 1 explains that the reindeer who came 4th and 5th in the race would end up in the bootcamp. Therefore, Reinald Deere came either 4th or 5th.

Clue 3 states that the only female reindeer came 3 places lower than Reinhard Deerow. This is to say that if Reinhard Deerow came 1st, the female reindeer came 4th; and if Reinhard Deerow came 2nd, the female reindeer came 5th. Clue 5 indicates that Reinhild Deersley was a female reindeer (it says that she would have been faster if it hadn't been for her distracted elf). Clue 5 also indicates that she did not come last. Therefore, she must have come 4th and, consequently, Reinhard Deerow must have come 1st.

We just established above the Reinald Deere came either 4th or 5th. However, we now know that Reinhild Deersley came 4th. Therefore, Reinald Deere must have come 5th.

Reindeer: Reinhard Deerow = Ranking: 1st
Reindeer: Reinhild Deersley = Ranking: 4th
Reindeer: Reinald Deere = Ranking: 5th

D. Clue 2 indicates that the elf-reindeer pair who won the race was knocked by Reinald Deere. We know from Explanation C that Reinhard Deerow came 1st. Therefore, it was Reinhard Deerow and his elf who were slowed down by being knocked by another reindeer.

Reindeer: Reinhard Deerow = Ranking: 1st = Slowed down by: Knocked down by another reindeer

E. Clue 4 indicates that Jingle Belle's finish time was 15 s less than her boyfriend's finish time of 4 mins 25 s. This is to say that Jingle Belle's finish time must have been 4 mins 10 s. Clue 7 states that the fastest race time was 4 mins 10 s. This is to say that Jingle Belle must have come 1st.

We know from Explanation D that Reinhard Deerow came 1st and the reason for being slowed down was being knocked by another reindeer. Since Jingle Belle came 1st, Reinhard Deerow must have been her reindeer and their reason for being slowed down was that they had been knocked by another reindeer.

Elf	Reindeer	Ranking	Slowed down by
Dashin Throothesnoe			Poor steering
Jingle Belle	Reinhard Deerow	1st	Knocked by another reindeer
Owot Fun			Falling over
Ryde Ansing			
Wunorse Openslae			

F. Clue 2 indicates that Reinald Deere's elf had a red ski suit. We know from Explanation A that Ryde Ansing had a red ski suit and that Jingle Belle's ski suit color is unknown. However, since we already know that Jingle Belle's reindeer was called Reinhard Deerow, Reinald Deere can't be her reindeer. Therefore, Reinald Deere must be Ryde Ansing's reindeer.

We know from Explanation C that Reinald Deere came 5th. Therefore, Ryde Ansing's ranking was also 5th.

Elf	Reindeer	Ranking	Slowed down by
Dashin Throothesnoe			Poor steering
Jingle Belle	Reinhard Deerow	1st	Knocked by another reindeer
Owot Fun			Falling over
Ryde Ansing	Reinald Deere	5th	
Wunorse Openslae			

G. Clue 3 states that Owot Fun came 1 place higher than the elf whose steering left much to be desired, but 1 place lower than Reinbert Deerling. We know that Reinhard Deerow came 1st and Reinald Deere came 5th. We also know from Explanation C that Reinhild Deersley came 4th. This means that Reinbert Deerling must have come either 2nd or 3rd:

1. If Reinbert Deerling came 2nd, Owot Fun must have come 3rd, and the elf with poor steering must have come 4th.
2. If Reinbert Deerling came 3rd, Owot Fun must have come 4th, and the elf with poor steering must have come 5th.

We know that it was Ryde Ansing who came 5th and Dashin Throothesnoe was the elf with poor steering. Therefore, Dashin Throothesnoe cannot have come 5th. It follows from this that Reinbert Deerling must have come 2nd, Owot Fun must have come 3rd, and the elf with poor steering – that is, Dashin Throothesnoe – must have come 4th.

We established in Explanation C that Reinhild Deersley came 4th. We now know that Dashin Throothesnoe came 4th. Therefore, Dashin Throothesnoe and Reinhild Deersley must have formed a pair.

Reindeer: Reinbert Deerling = Ranking: 2nd

Elf	Reindeer	Ranking	Slowed down by
Dashin Throothesnoe	Reinhild Deersley	4th	Poor steering
Jingle Belle	Reinhard Deerow	1st	Knocked by another reindeer
Owot Fun		3rd	Falling over
Ryde Ansing	Reinald Deere	5th	
Wunorse Openslae			

H. We know that Dashin Throothesnoe was 4th, Jingle Belle was 1st, Owot Fun was 3rd, and Ryde Ansing was 5th. Therefore, it must be Wunorse Openslae who was 2nd.

We established in Explanation G that Reinbert Deerling came 2nd. Since Wunorse Openslae came 2nd, Reinbert Deerling must be his reindeer.

Since Dashin Throothesnoe's reindeer was Reinhild Deersley, Jingle Belle's reindeer was Reinhard Deerow, Ryde Ansing's reindeer was Reinald Deere, and Wunorse Openslae's reindeer was Reinbert Deerling, it must be Owot Fun's reindeer that was Reinbald Deerey.

Elf	Reindeer	Ranking	Slowed down by
Dashin Throothesnoe	Reinhild Deersley	4th	Poor steering
Jingle Belle	Reinhard Deerow	1st	Knocked by another reindeer
Owot Fun	Reinbald Deerey	3rd	Falling over
Ryde Ansing	Reinald Deere	5th	
Wunorse Openslae	Reinbert Deerling	2nd	

I. Clue 4 mentions Jingle Belle and her boyfriend whose skis were too slippery. Since Dashin Throothesnoe was slowed down by poor steering and Owot Fun was slowed down by falling over, these 2 elves cannot be Jingle Belle's boyfriend. It follows from this that it was either Ryde Ansing or Wunorse Openslaè who was Jingle Belle's boyfriend and whose skis were too slippery. Clue 4 states that Jingle Belle's boyfriend's finish time was 4 mins 25 s. We know that Ryde Ansing came 5th and Wunorse Openslae came 2nd. We don't know Jingle Belle's boyfriend's ranking, but Clue 5 states that Reinhild Deersley's racing time was 5 mins 22 s. This is more than the boyfriend's time of 4 mins 25 s. This means that the boyfriend cannot have come last – that is, 5th. It follows from this that Jingle Belle's boyfriend must be Wunorse Openslae who came 2nd, and it was Wunorse Openslae whose skis were too slippery.

Since Dashin Throothesnoe was slowed down by poor steering, Jingle Belle was knocked down by another reindeer, Owot Fun fell over, and Wunorse Openslae's skis were too slippery, it must be Ryde Ansing who was slowed

down by a non-aerodynamic ski suit.

Elf	Reindeer	Ranking	Slowed down by
Dashin Throothesnoe	Reinhild Deersley	4th	Poor steering
Jingle Belle	Reinhard Deerow	1st	Knocked by another reindeer
Owot Fun	Reinbald Deerey	3rd	Falling over
Ryde Ansing	Reinald Deere	5th	Non-aerodynamic ski suit
Wunorse Openslae	Reinbert Deerling	2nd	Too slippery skis

10. Oh Christmas Tea, Oh Christmas Tea

A. Clue 1 explains that Mrs Claus' jar labels had been turned upside down. This means that the original jar numbers mostly became different numbers in their upside-down orientation. (If you rotate the page 180 degrees from how you would view the numbers in the logic grid normally, you can see what the upside-down numbers are.)

16 became 91
61 became 19
91 became 16
96 became 96 (i.e. this number remained the same before and after the elves' break-in)
98 became 86

Clue 1 also explains that jars numbered 1–25 were on the 1st shelf (which was the top shelf), the jars numbered 26–50 were on the 2nd shelf, the jars numbered 51–75 were on the 3rd shelf, and the jars numbered 76–100 were on the 4th shelf (which was the lowest shelf). When we look at the original jar numbers, the jars were on the following shelves:

Shelf 1 (top shelf): 16
Shelf 2: –
Shelf 3: 61
Shelf 4 (lowest shelf): 91, 96, and 98

When we look at the upside-down numbers, the jars were on the following shelves:

Shelf 1 (top shelf): 16 and 19
Shelf 2: –
Shelf 3: –
Shelf 4 (lowest shelf): 86, 91, and 96

B. Clue 3 indicates that Mrs Claus planned to use nutmeg for Nutmeg Nog.

Tea blend	Original jar no.	Original spice	New spice
Berry and Bright			
Most Wonderful Lime			
Mulled Pine			
Nutmeg Nog		Nutmeg	
Naughty or Spice			

C. Clue 7 states that the jar number for Naughty or Spice's spice was higher before and after the elves' break-in than the original and upside-down numbers of the jar where cardamom should have been. Clue 7 further indicates that the Naughty or Spice's spice jar wasn't the one whose number remained the same even when its label was turned upside down. This is to say that Naughty or Spice's spice jar cannot have been number 96 as this number remained the same when turned upside down. It follows from this that there is only 1 combination that is feasible: for Naughty or Spice's spice jar to be numbered higher than the jar that originally contained cardamom before and after the elves' break-in, its original number had to be 98 (which became 86 when turned upside down) and the original number of the jar originally containing cardamom had to be 61 (which became 19 when turned upside down).

Original jar no: 61 = Original spice: Cardamom

Tea blend	Original jar no.	Original spice	New spice
Berry and Bright			
Most Wonderful Lime			
Mulled Pine			
Nutmeg Nog		Nutmeg	
Naughty or Spice	98		

D. Clue 8 states that cayenne pepper and nutmeg were in 2 jars whose numbers were transposed when the labels were turned upside down. When we look at Explanation A, we can see that the jar originally numbered 16 became 91 when its label was turned upside down, and the jar originally numbered 91 became 16. So, the 2 jars to which Clue 8 refers to are 16 and 91. We can rephrase the clue as follows: cayenne pepper and nutmeg were in jars whose original numbers were 16 and 91 (but not necessarily in this order).

Clue 4 states that the jars now containing cayenne pepper and paprika were originally on the 1st and 3rd shelves (but not necessarily in this order). When we look at Explanation A, we can see that the jars in question were 16 (1st shelf) and 61 (3rd shelf).

We have just established that of cayenne pepper and nutmeg, one was in a jar originally numbered 16 and the other was in a jar originally numbered 91 (but not necessarily in this order). We have also established that of cayenne pepper and paprika, one was in a jar originally numbered 16 and the other was in a jar originally numbered 61 (but not necessarily in this order). When we combine these pieces of information, we can deduce that cayenne pepper must have been in a jar originally numbered 16. It follows from this that nutmeg must have been in a jar that was originally numbered 91 and paprika must have been in a jar that was originally numbered 61.

We now know that nutmeg's original jar number was 91 and that nutmeg was used for Nutmeg Nog. Therefore, Nutmeg Nog's spice was in the jar originally numbered 91.

Original jar no: 16 = New spice: Cayenne pepper
Original jar no: 61 = New spice: Paprika

Tea blend	Original jar no.	Original spice	New spice
Berry and Bright			
Most Wonderful Lime			
Mulled Pine			
Nutmeg Nog	91	Nutmeg	
Naughty or Spice	98		

E. Clue 5 indicates that the upside-down number of the jar where mustard was placed was 5 numbers lower than the upside-down number of the spice for Most Wonderful Lime. We know that the original number of the jar for Nutmeg Nog's spice was 91 and the original number of the jar for Naughty or Spice's spice was 98. Therefore, the original number of the jar for Most Wonderful Lime's spice must have been 16, 61, or 96. The upside-down numbers of these numbers are: 91, 19, and 96. For mustard to be placed in a jar whose upside-down number was 5 lower than the upside-down number of the jar for Most Wonderful Lime's spice – that is, 91, 19, or 96 – the upside-down number of the jar where mustard was placed must have been 86, 14, or 91. Since 14 is not a listed option (see Explanation A), the mustard jar's upside-down number must have been either 86 or 91. However, we established in Explanation D that the cayenne pepper's jar's upside-down number was 91 (i.e. its original number was 16). Therefore, the mustard jar's upside-down number must have been 86 – which means its original number must have been 98. It follows from this that the upside-down number of the spice for Most Wonderful Lime must have been 91 (i.e. 5 higher than 86) – which means that its original jar number must have been 16.

We now know that the original jar number for Naughty or Spice's spice was 98, which is the same number, as we just established, as the spice where mustard was placed. Therefore, the elves had put mustard into the spice jar originally numbered 98 which should have contained Naughty or Spice's original spice.

We know from Explanation D that cayenne pepper was in a jar whose original number was 16. In other words, this jar's number was the same as the

spice jar number for Most Wonderful Lime's spice, as established above. Therefore, the elves had put cayenne pepper into the spice jar originally numbered 16 which should have contained Most Wonderful Lime's original spice.

Tea blend	Original jar no.	Original spice	New spice
Berry and Bright			
Most Wonderful Lime	16		Cayenne pepper
Mulled Pine			
Nutmeg Nog	91	Nutmeg	
Naughty or Spice	98		Mustard

F. Clue 6 states that the elves avoided replacing original jar contents with spices whose names started with the same letter. This is to say that cayenne pepper was not put in a jar where cardamom, cinnamon, or cloves had been. Also, we know that cayenne pepper was not in the same jar where nutmeg had been as nutmeg had been meant for Nutmeg Nog and cayenne pepper was in a jar where Most Wonderful Lime's spice should have been. It follows from this that cayenne pepper was put in a jar where ginger should have been. Since cayenne pepper was in a jar meant for Most Wonderful Lime and since this is where ginger should have been, it must have been ginger that Mrs Claus meant to use for Most Wonderful Lime.

Tea blend	Original jar no.	Original spice	New spice
Berry and Bright			
Most Wonderful Lime	16	Ginger	Cayenne pepper
Mulled Pine			
Nutmeg Nog	91	Nutmeg	
Naughty or Spice	98		Mustard

G. Clue 6 states that the elves avoided replacing original jar contents with spices whose names started with the same letter. This means that cumin cannot have been put in a jar where cardamom, cinnamon, or cloves had been. As we know that cayenne pepper was put in ginger's jar, we can deduce that cumin must have been placed in the jar where nutmeg used to be. We know that nutmeg was the spice meant for Nutmeg Nog. Therefore, cumin must have been placed in this jar.

Tea blend	Original jar no.	Original spice	New spice
Berry and Bright			
Most Wonderful Lime	16	Ginger	Cayenne pepper
Mulled Pine			
Nutmeg Nog	91	Nutmeg	Cumin
Naughty or Spice	98		Mustard

H. Clue 2 indicates that of the 2 jars on the top shelf after the elves' break-in, one should have contained the spice for Mulled Pine. We know that the original spice jar number of Most Wonderful Lime was 16, the original spice jar number of Nutmeg Nog was 91, and the original spice jar number of Naughty or Spice was 98. This means that the original spice jar number of Mulled Pine was either 61 or 96. After the elves had turned the labels upside down, these numbers became 19 and 96. Since the spice jar for Mulled Pine was on the top shelf after the elves' break-in, it must have been the jar with an upside-down number of 19 (we established in Explanation A that the jar with an upside-down number of 19 was placed on the top shelf). This upside-down number's original number was 61. It follows from this that the original jar number for Mulled Pine's spice must have been 61.

Since the original jar number for Most Wonderful Lime's spice was 16, the original jar number for Mulled Pine's spice was 61, the original jar number for Nutmeg Nog's spice was 91, and the original jar number for Naughty or Spice's spice was 98, it must be the original jar number for Berry and Bright's spice that was 96.

Tea blend	Original jar no.	Original spice	New spice
Berry and Bright	96		
Most Wonderful Lime	16	Ginger	Cayenne pepper
Mulled Pine	61		
Nutmeg Nog	91	Nutmeg	Cumin
Naughty or Spice	98		Mustard

I. We established in Explanation C that the original spice in the jar originally numbered 61 was cardamom. We now know that this was the jar where Mulled Pine's spice was meant to be. Therefore, cardamom must have been the original spice in Mulled Pine.

We established in Explanation D that the new spice in the jar originally numbered 61 was paprika. We now know that this was the jar where Mulled Pine's spice was meant to be. Therefore, paprika must have been the spice that the elves put in the jar meant for Mulled Pine's spice.

We now know that the new spice in the jar meant for Most Wonderful Lime's spice was cayenne pepper, the new spice in the jar meant for Mulled Pine's spice was paprika, the new spice in the jar meant for Nutmeg Nog's spice was cumin, and the new spice in the jar meant for Naughty or Spice's spice was mustard. Therefore, the new spice in the jar meant for Berry and Bright's spice must have been garam masala.

Tea blend	Original jar no.	Original spice	New spice
Berry and Bright	96		Garam masala
Most Wonderful Lime	16	Ginger	Cayenne pepper
Mulled Pine	61	Cardamom	Paprika
Nutmeg Nog	91	Nutmeg	Cumin
Naughty or Spice	98		Mustard

J. Clue 3 indicates that the jar whose number remained the same when turned upside down should have contained a spice that had 1 more M letter in it than the original spice in a jar that sat before and after the elves' naughty visit on the bottom shelf. This is to say that there were 2 original spices in 2 jars, and the number of one of these jars remained the same when turned upside down and the other jar sat on the bottom shelf both before and after the elves' naughty visit.

We established in Explanation A that the jar numbered 96 remained the same number when turned upside down. Let's call this the 1st jar. To figure out what the 2nd jar's number was, we need to determine which jar would have sat on the bottom shelf both before and after the elves' break-in. We established in Explanation A that jars numbered 76-100 would have sat on the bottom shelf, and that the jar numbered 98 became 86 when turned upside down. Therefore, this jar – which we'll call the 2nd jar – would have been the jar originally numbered 98. (The jar numbered 96 – i.e. the jar we named the 1st jar – would also have sat on the bottom shelf both before and after the elves' break-in, but since this 1st jar is compared to the 2nd jar, these 2 jars cannot be the same.)

Now that we have established that the 1st jar was numbered 96 (both before and after the mischievous elves' visit) and the 2nd jar was originally numbered 98, we can rephrase Clue 3 as follows: the original spice that was in the jar numbered 96 contained 1 more letter M than the original spice in the jar originally numbered 98. We know that that ginger was the original spice in the jar numbered 16, cardamom was in the jar numbered 61, and nutmeg was in the jar numbered 91. Therefore, of the jars originally numbered 96 and 98, one must have contained cinnamon and the other cloves. We can see that the word cinnamon contains 1 more M letter than the word cloves. It follows from this that the original spice in the jar numbered 96 must have been cinnamon and the original spice in the jar originally numbered 98 must have been cloves.

Tea blend	Original jar no.	Original spice	New spice
Berry and Bright	96	Cinnamon	Garam masala
Most Wonderful Lime	16	Ginger	Cayenne pepper
Mulled Pine	61	Cardamom	Paprika
Nutmeg Nog	91	Nutmeg	Cumin
Naughty or Spice	98	Cloves	Mustard

11. Truly, Medley, Deeply

A. Clue 4 indicates that the illness that affected Tinsel Troop's elves was tinsellitis.

Clue 1 states that Lil' Drummer Dudettes had 4 more singers present than the all-male choir, but fewer performers than the choir whose 1st song in their medley was *Jingle Bell Sock*. Since there was another choir who had more singers performing, this means that Lil' Drummer Dudettes cannot have had the most healthy elves on stage: in other words, Lil' Drummer Dudettes cannot have had 20 healthy elves. When we look at the rest of the options for the number of healthy elves in the grid, there is only 1 combination where Lil' Drummer Dudettes had 4 more singers present than the all-male choir: Lil' Drummer Dudettes must have had 13 healthy elves performing and the all-male choir must have had 9 healthy elves performing (we don't know yet the name of the all-male choir).

As mentioned above, Lil' Drummer Dudettes had fewer performers than the choir whose 1st song in their medley was *Jingle Bell Sock*. Since we now know that Lil' Drummer Dudettes had 13 healthy elves performing, the choir whose 1st song in their medley was *Jingle Bell Sock* must have had either 16 or 20 healthy elves.

All-male choir = Healthy elves: 9
First song: Jingle Bell Sock = Healthy elves: 16 OR 20

Choir	First song	Illness	Healthy elves
Lil' Drummer Dudettes			13
Mistletoe Mania			
Poinsettia Posse			
Roasted Chestnuts			
Tinsel Troop		Tinsellitis	

B. Clue 6 states that the combined number of ill elves belonging to Roasted Chestnuts and the choir whose 1st song was *All I Want for Christmas Is Food* was 30 more elves than the ill elves in the choir whose 1st song was *All the Jingle Ladies*. The grid tells us the number of healthy elves, but this clue contains information about ill elves. Clue 1 explains that each choir was supposed to consist of 23 singers, but none had their full membership present. Therefore, we can work out the number of ill elves by deducting the number of healthy elves from 23:

Healthy elves: 4 = Ill elves: 19
Healthy elves: 9 = Ill elves: 14
Healthy elves: 13 = Ill elves: 10
Healthy elves: 16 = Ill elves: 7
Healthy elves: 20 = Ill elves: 3

When we look at the number of ill elves, there is only 1 combination where the combined number of ill elves belonging to Roasted Chestnuts and the choir whose 1st song was *All I Want for Christmas Is Food* was 30 more elves than the ill elves in the choir whose 1st song was *All the Jingle Ladies*: the number of ill elves belonging to Roasted Chestnuts and the choir whose 1st song was *All I Want for Christmas Is Food* must have been 19 and 14 (but not necessarily in this order) and the number of ill elves in the choir whose 1st song was *All the Jingle Ladies* must have been 3 (19 ill elves + 14 ill elves = 33 ill elves – which is 30 more than 3).

As the puzzle asks us about the number of healthy elves, we have to figure out what these numbers of ill elves mean in terms of how many healthy elves there were. If we look at the list we worked out above, we can see that 19 ill elves mean that there were 4 healthy elves, 14 ill elves mean that there were 9 healthy elves, and 3 ill elves mean that there were 20 healthy elves. This is to say that of Roasted Chestnuts and the choir whose 1st song was *All I Want for Christmas Is Food,* one had 4 and the other 9 healthy elves, while the choir whose 1st song was *All the Jingle Ladies* had 20 healthy elves.

Choir: Roasted Chestnuts = Healthy elves: 4 OR 9
First song: All I Want for Christmas Is Food = Healthy elves: 4 OR 9
First song: All the Jingle Ladies = Healthy elves: 20

C. Clue 3 states that *Santa Claus Is Humming, "Calm Down."* was the 1st song that was sung by a choir whose performers on the night did not outnumber the choir whose members suffered from mince pie malady. Clue 3 also states that the latter choir was a male-voice choir. In other words, *Santa Claus Is Humming, "Calm Down."* was the 1st song that was sung by a choir whose performers on the night did not outnumber the male-voice choir. We established in Explanation A that the male-voice choir had 9 elves performing. For the choir whose 1st song was *Santa Claus Is Humming, "Calm Down."* to not outnumber the male-voice choir's 9 healthy elves, it must have had 4 healthy elves performing.

We established in Explanation B that the choir whose 1st song was *All I Want for Christmas Is Food* had either 4 or 9 healthy elves performing. Now that we know that it was the choir whose 1st song in their medley was *Santa Claus Is Humming, "Calm Down."* that had 4 healthy elves performing, we can deduce that the choir whose 1st song was *All I Want for Christmas Is Food* must have had 9 healthy elves performing.

We know from Explanation A that the all-male choir had 9 healthy elves performing, and we have just established that the choir whose 1st song was *All I Want for Christmas Is Food* had 9 healthy elves performing. Therefore, it was the all-male choir that sang *All I Want for Christmas Is Food* as their 1st song.

As established above in the 1st paragraph, Clue 3 indicates that the all-male choir was affected by mince pie malady.

All-male choir = First song: All I Want for Christmas Is Food = Illness: Mince pie malady = Healthy elves: 9
First song: Santa Claus Is Humming, "Calm Down." = Healthy elves: 4

D. We established in Explanation B that of Roasted Chestnuts and the choir whose 1st song was *All I Want for Christmas Is Food*, one had 4 and the other 9 healthy elves. We established in Explanation C that the all-male choir, whose 1st song was *All I Want for Christmas Is Food*, had 9 healthy elves performing. Therefore, Roasted Chestnuts must have had 4 healthy elves performing.

We established in Explanation C that the choir whose 1st song was *Santa Claus Is Humming, "Calm Down."* had 4 healthy elves performing. We now know that Roasted Chestnuts had 4 healthy elves performing. Therefore, Roasted Chestnuts' 1st song must have been *Santa Claus Is Humming, "Calm Down."*.

Choir	First song	Illness	Healthy elves
Lil' Drummer Dudettes			13
Mistletoe Mania			
Poinsettia Posse			
Roasted Chestnuts	Santa Claus Is Humming, "Calm Down."		4
Tinsel Troop		Tinsellitis	

E. Clue 5 indicates that the choir whose members were struck by mistletoe malaise was either Poinsettia Posse or the choir whose 1st song was *Freeze a Jolly Good Fellow*: if it was the former, 7 members of Poinsettia Posse became ill; if, instead, it was the latter, this choir was the all-male choir. We know from Explanation C that the all-male choir's 1st song was *All I Want for Christmas Is Food*. This is to say, it was not *Freeze a Jolly Good Fellow*. Therefore, the choir struck by mistletoe malaise cannot have been the all-male choir. Instead, it must have been Poinsettia Posse whose members were struck by mistletoe malaise and 7 members of their choir became ill. We established in Explanation B that 7 ill elves meant that there were 16 healthy elves left in the choir. Therefore, it was Poinsettia Posse who had 16 healthy elves performing on the night while the ill elves suffered from mistletoe malaise.

Choir	First song	Illness	Healthy elves
Lil' Drummer Dudettes			13
Mistletoe Mania			
Poinsettia Posse		Mistletoe malaise	16
Roasted Chestnuts	Santa Claus Is Humming, "Calm Down."		4
Tinsel Troop		Tinsellitis	

F. Clue 4 indicates that, among Tinsel Troop's members, 7 fewer members than the elves acquiring ice dance fever were left with tinsellitis. In other words, there were 7 more elves affected by ice dance fever than tinsellitis.

We know that Lil' Drummer Dudettes had 13 healthy elves, Mistletoe Mania had 16 healthy elves, and Roasted Chestnuts had 4 healthy elves. It

follows from this that Tinsel Troop, whose elves were affected by tinsellitis, had either 9 or 20 healthy elves. We established in Explanation B that 9 healthy elves meant that there were 14 ill elves, and 20 healthy elves meant that there were 3 ill elves. So, Tinsel Troop had either 14 or 3 elves affected by tinsellitis.

For there to be 7 more elves who were affected by ice dance fever than tinsellitis, the only combination that is feasible is that 3 elves among Tinsel Troop's elves were affected by tinsellitis and 10 elves were affected by ice dance fever. What this means in terms of healthy elves is that there were 20 healthy elves in Tinsel Troop and 13 healthy elves in the choir that was affected by ice dance fever.

We know that Lil' Drummer Dudettes had 13 healthy elves performing and we now also know that the choir that had 13 healthy elves was affected by ice dance fever. Therefore, it was Lil' Drummer Dudettes who were affected by ice dance fever.

Choir	First song	Illness	Healthy elves
Lil' Drummer Dudettes		Ice dance fever	13
Mistletoe Mania			
Poinsettia Posse		Mistletoe malaise	16
Roasted Chestnuts	Santa Claus Is Humming, "Calm Down."		4
Tinsel Troop		Tinsellitis	20

G. We know that Lil' Drummer Dudettes had 13 healthy elves performing, Poinsettia Posse had 16 healthy elves performing, Roasted Chestnuts had 4 healthy elves performing, and Tinsel Troop had 20 healthy elves performing. Therefore, Mistletoe Mania must have had 9 healthy elves performing.

We established in Explanation C that the all-male choir had 9 healthy elves performing and that their 1st song was *All I Want for Christmas Is Food*, and that they were affected by mince pie malady. Now that we know that Mistletoe Mania had 9 healthy elves performing, we can deduce that it must be Mistletoe Mania that was the all-male choir whose 1st song was *All I Want for Christmas Is Food* and who were affected by mince pie malady.

Choir	First song	Illness	Healthy elves
Lil' Drummer Dudettes		Ice dance fever	13
Mistletoe Mania	All I Want for Christmas Is Food	Mince pie malady	9
Poinsettia Posse		Mistletoe malaise	16
Roasted Chestnuts	Santa Claus Is Humming, "Calm Down."		4
Tinsel Troop		Tinsellitis	20

H. We know that Lil' Drummer Dudettes were affected by ice dance fever, Mistletoe Mania was affected by mince pie malady, Poinsettia Posse was affected by mistletoe malaise, and Tinsel Troop was affected by tinsellitis. Therefore, it must be Roasted Chestnuts who were affected by figgy pudding feebleness.

Choir	First song	Illness	Healthy elves
Lil' Drummer Dudettes		Ice dance fever	13
Mistletoe Mania	All I Want for Christmas Is Food	Mince pie malady	9
Poinsettia Posse		Mistletoe malaise	16
Roasted Chestnuts	Santa Claus Is Humming, "Calm Down."	Figgy pudding feebleness	4
Tinsel Troop		Tinsellitis	20

I. We established in Explanation B that the choir whose 1st song was *All the Jingle Ladies* had 20 healthy elves performing. We now know that Tinsel Troop had 20 healthy elves performing. Therefore, Tinsel Troop's 1st song must have been *All the Jingle Ladies*.

We established in Explanation A that the choir whose 1st song was *Jingle Bell Sock* had either 16 or 20 healthy elves performing. We now know that Tinsel Troop had 20 healthy elves performing and their 1st song was *All the Jingle Ladies*. Therefore, the choir whose 1st song was *Jingle Bell Sock* must have had 16 healthy elves performing. We now know that Poinsettia

Posse had 16 healthy elves performing. Therefore, Poinsettia Posse's 1st song must have been *Jingle Bell Sock*.

Choir	First song	Illness	Healthy elves
Lil' Drummer Dudettes		Ice dance fever	13
Mistletoe Mania	All I Want for Christmas Is Food	Mince pie malady	9
Poinsettia Posse	Jingle Bell Sock	Mistletoe malaise	16
Roasted Chestnuts	Santa Claus Is Humming, "Calm Down."	Figgy pudding feebleness	4
Tinsel Troop	All the Jingle Ladies	Tinsellitis	20

J. We know that Mistletoe Mania's 1st song was *All I Want for Christmas Is Food*, Poinsettia Posse's 1st song was *Jingle Bell Sock*, Roasted Chestnuts' 1st song was *Santa Claus Is Humming, "Calm Down."*, and Tinsel Troop's 1st song was *All the Jingle Ladies*. Therefore, Lil' Drummer Dudettes' 1st song must have been *Freeze a Jolly Good Fellow*.

Choir	First song	Illness	Healthy elves
Lil' Drummer Dudettes	Freeze a Jolly Good Fellow	Ice dance fever	13
Mistletoe Mania	All I Want for Christmas Is Food	Mince pie malady	9
Poinsettia Posse	Jingle Bell Sock	Mistletoe malaise	16
Roasted Chestnuts	Santa Claus Is Humming, "Calm Down."	Figgy pudding feebleness	4
Tinsel Troop	All the Jingle Ladies	Tinsellitis	20

12. I Only Have Ice for You

A. Clue 1 indicates that *An Elfie Stick* was deemed "Un-fir-gettable" by the judges.

Sculpture	Page section	Ranking	Comment
An Elfie Stick			"Un-fir-gettable"
Bear-y Christmas!			
Christmas Fishes			
Kissing under the Mistletoad			
No Time Like the Present			

B. This puzzle has clues that require us to figure out how many icy elements each ice sculpture had. Clue 1 indicates that *An Elfie Stick* was a solitary climbing pole. This means that *An Elfie Stick* had 1 icy element. Clue 1 also mentions that there was a sculpture featuring 30 intertwined bears and Clue 5 indicates that the bear-themed sculpture was called *Bear-y Christmas!* Hence, *Bear-y Christmas!* had 30 icy elements.

Clue 3 indicates that *Christmas Fishes* consisted of 12 fish. Therefore, *Christmas Fishes* had 12 icy elements. Clue 5 states that *Kissing under the Mistletoad* featured a giant toad. This refers to just 1 icy element. Clue 6 states that *No Time Like the Present* consisted of 20 present-shaped cubes. This means that it had 20 icy elements.

Sculpture: An Elfie Stick = Icy elements: 1
Sculpture: Bear-y Christmas! = Icy elements: 30
Sculpture: Christmas Fishes = Icy elements: 12
Sculpture: Kissing under the Mistletoad = Icy elements: 1
Sculpture: No Time Like the Present = Icy elements: 20

C. Clue 4 states that "The myrrh the merrier" and "Love at frost sight" were not heard in connection with sculptures that contained either 30 or 12 icy elements. We know from Explanation B that *Bear-y Christmas!* had 30 icy elements and *Christmas Fishes* had 12 icy elements. Therefore, *Bear-y Christmas!* and *Christmas Fishes* did not receive the comments "The myrrh the merrier" and "Love at frost sight". Since *An Elfie Stick* got the comment "Un-fir-gettable", *Bear-y Christmas!* and *Christmas Fishes* cannot have received that comment either. It follows from this that of *Bear-y Christmas!*

and *Christmas Fishes*, one must have got the comment "A round of Santa-plause" and the other must have got the comment "Santamental" (but not necessarily in this order).

Clue 3 compares *Christmas Fishes* with a sculpture that received the comment "A round of Santa-plause". This means that *Christmas Fishes* cannot have received the comment "A round of Santa-plause". Therefore, it must have received the comment "Santamental". It follows from this that *Bear-y Christmas!* must have got the comment "A round of Santa-plause".

Sculpture	Page section	Ranking	Comment
An Elfie Stick			"Un-fir-gettable"
Bear-y Christmas!			"A round of Santa-plause"
Christmas Fishes			"Santamental"
Kissing under the Mistletoad			
No Time Like the Present			

D. Clue 7 states that of the 2 sculptures consisting of only 1 icy element, one came 1st and the other's photo was in Section E. We know from Explanation B that the sculptures that only had 1 icy element were *An Elfie Stick* and *Kissing under the Mistletoad*. This is to say, of *An Elfie Stick* and *Kissing under the Mistletoad*, one came 1st and the other's photo was in Section E. Clue 1 indicates that *An Elfie Stick* came 2 places lower that the sculpture featuring bears. This means that *An Elfie Stick* cannot have come 1st. Therefore, *Kissing under the Mistletoad* must have come 1st. It follows from this that *An Elfie Stick* must have been placed in Section E on the page.

Sculpture	Page section	Ranking	Comment
An Elfie Stick	E		"Un-fir-gettable"
Bear-y Christmas!			"A round of Santa-plause"
Christmas Fishes			"Santamental"
Kissing under the Mistletoad		1st	
No Time Like the Present			

E. We know that the comment about *An Elfie Stick* was "Un-fir-gettable", the comment about *Bear-y Christmas!* was "A round of Santa-plause", and the comment about *Christmas Fishes* was "Santamental". Therefore, of *Kissing under the Mistletoad* and *No Time Like the Present*, one's comment was "Love at Frost Sight" and the other's comment was "The myrrh the merrier" (but not necessarily in this order). Clue 2 indicates that the judges didn't think that "The myrrh the merrier" was an apt description for the winning sculpture. We know that *Kissing under the Mistletoad* came 1st, so that was the winning sculpture, and so, its comment was not "The myrrh the merrier". Therefore, its comment must have been "Love at frost sight". It follows from this that the comment about *No Time Like the Present* must have been "The myrrh the merrier".

Sculpture	Page section	Ranking	Comment
An Elfie Stick	E		"Un-fir-gettable"
Bear-y Christmas!			"A round of Santa-plause"
Christmas Fishes			"Santamental"
Kissing under the Mistletoad		1st	"Love at frost sight"
No Time Like the Present			"The myrrh the merrier"

F. We know that *Kissing under the Mistletoad* came 1st. Clue 5 indicates that the kids placed this sculpture 1 place higher than the sculpture whose photo was placed right above *Bear-y Christmas!* Another way to express this is that the sculpture whose photo was right above *Bear-y Christmas!* came 2nd. We can deduce from these pieces of information that *Bear-y Christmas!* cannot have come 1st or 2nd. Therefore, it must have come 3rd, 4th, or 5th.

Clue 1 indicates that *An Elfie Stick* was ranked 2 places lower than the bear sculpture which, we know, is called *Bear-y Christmas!* The only way this is feasible is if *Bear-y Christmas!* – given that it must have come 3rd, 4th, or

5th – came 3rd and *An Elfie Stick* came 5th.

Sculpture	Page section	Ranking	Comment
An Elfie Stick	E	5th	"Un-fir-gettable"
Bear-y Christmas!		3rd	"A round of Santa-plause"
Christmas Fishes			"Santamental"
Kissing under the Mistletoad		1st	"Love at frost sight"
No Time Like the Present			"The myrrh the merrier"

G. Clue 3 indicates that the photos of *Christmas Fishes* and the photo of the sculpture that was commented as deserving "A round of Santa-plause" touched the section where the 5th-ranking sculpture was placed. We know that the 5th-ranking sculpture was *An Elfie Stick* and that it was in Section E. We also know that the comment relating to *Bear-y Christmas!* was "A round of Santa-plause". Therefore, we can rephrase the clue as follows: the photos of *Christmas Fishes* and *Bear-y Christmas!* touched Section E. When we look at the diagram, we can see that Sections B, C, and D touch Section E. Hence, *Christmas Fishes* and *Bear-y Christmas!* were in Sections B, C, or D.

Clue 2 indicates that the winning sculpture was placed in a section that was in portrait orientation. When we look at the diagram, we can see that the portrait sections are Sections B and D. Hence, the winning sculpture – which we know was *Kissing under the Mistletoad* – was either in Section B or D.

We know that *An Elfie Stick* was in Section E. We have now also established that *Christmas Fishes* and *Bear-y Christmas!* were in Sections B, C, or D, and *Kissing under the Mistletoad* was either in Section B or D. This means that *No Time Like the Present* must have been in Section A.

Sculpture: Christmas Fishes = Page section: B, C, OR D
Sculpture: Bear-y Christmas! = Page section: B, C, OR D
Sculpture: Kissing under the Mistletoad = Page section: B OR D

Sculpture	Page section	Ranking	Comment
An Elfie Stick	E	5th	"Un-fir-gettable"
Bear-y Christmas!		3rd	"A round of Santa-plause"
Christmas Fishes			"Santamental"
Kissing under the Mistletoad		1st	"Love at frost sight"
No Time Like the Present	A		"The myrrh the merrier"

H. Clue 6 indicates that the photo of *No Time Like the Present* was not adjacent to the photo of the sculpture that came 4th. We know that the photo of *No Time Like the Present* was in Section A. Section A is adjacent to Sections B and C, but not Sections D and E. Therefore, the photo of the sculpture that came 4th must have been in Section D or E. However, we already know that the photo of the 5th-ranking sculpture, *An Elfie Stick*, was in Section E. Hence, the photo of the 4th-ranking sculpture must have been in Section D.

Clue 6 further indicates that the photo of *No Time Like the Present* and the photo of the sculpture that came 4th both touched the photo of the 3rd-ranking sculpture. Since we now know that the photo of the 4th-ranking sculpture was in Section D and *No Time Like the Present* was in Section A, we can see by looking at the diagram that the only section that they both touch is Section C. Therefore, it is in Section C that the photo of the 3rd-ranking sculpture was placed. We know that *Bear-y Christmas!* came 3rd. Hence, it was the photo of *Bear-y Christmas!* that was placed in Section C.

Page section: D = Ranking: 4th

Sculpture	Page section	Ranking	Comment
An Elfie Stick	E	5th	"Un-fir-gettable"
Bear-y Christmas!	C	3rd	"A round of Santa-plause"
Christmas Fishes			"Santamental"
Kissing under the Mistletoad		1st	"Love at frost sight"
No Time Like the Present	A		"The myrrh the merrier"

I. We now know that *An Elfie Stick* came 5th, *Bear-y Christmas!* came 3rd, and *Kissing under the Mistletoad* came 1st. Therefore, of *Christmas Fishes* and *No Time Like the Present*, one came 2nd and the other 4th (but not necessarily in this order). We established in Explanation H that the photo of the 4th-ranking sculpture was placed in Section D. Since we know that the photo of *No Time Like the Present* was placed in Section A, it cannot have come 4th. Therefore, it must have come 2nd. It follows from this that *Christmas Fishes* must have come 4th and its photo must have been placed in Section D.

Sculpture	Page section	Ranking	Comment
An Elfie Stick	E	5th	"Un-fir-gettable"
Bear-y Christmas!	C	3rd	"A round of Santa-plause"
Christmas Fishes	D	4th	"Santamental"
Kissing under the Mistletoad		1st	"Love at frost sight"
No Time Like the Present	A	2nd	"The myrrh the merrier"

J. We now know that the photo of *An Elfie Stick* was in Section E, the photo of *Bear-y Christmas!* was in Section C, the photo of *Christmas Fishes* was in Section D, and the photo of *No Time Like the Present* was in Section A. Therefore, the photo of *Kissing under the Mistletoad* must had been in Section B.

Sculpture	Page section	Ranking	Comment
An Elfie Stick	E	5th	"Un-fir-gettable"
Bear-y Christmas!	C	3rd	"A round of Santa-plause"
Christmas Fishes	D	4th	"Santamental"
Kissing under the Mistletoad	B	1st	"Love at frost sight"
No Time Like the Present	A	2nd	"The myrrh the merrier"

13. Elf and Safety

A. Clue 1 indicates that there were 2 elves whom Brave Dave met over the weekend: one was too busy taking elfies and another wasn't mistletoeing the line. This is to say that of the elves who were too busy taking elfies and not mistletoeing the line, one was seen by Brave Dave on Saturday and the other one on Sunday (but not necessarily in this order).

Clue 1 also indicates that Brave Dave had seen the elf who was taking elfies on a ladder 3 days before their meeting took place. Furthermore, Clue 3 indicates that the elf responsible for the Quizmas Committee saw the elfie-taking elf on a ladder as he was walking out of Brave Dave's office. This is to say that the elf responsible for the Quizmas Committee met Brave Dave 3 days earlier than the elf taking elfies met Brave Dave. Since we know that the elf taking elfies met Brave Dave either on Saturday or Sunday, the elf responsible for the Quizmas Committee must have met Brave Dave either on Wednesday or Thursday respectively. Since Wednesday is not an option in the grid, the elf responsible for the Quizmas Committee must have met Brave Dave on Thursday and the elf who was too busy taking elfies must have met Brave Dave on Sunday.

We established above that the elf who wasn't mistletoeing the line met Brave Dave on Saturday or Sunday. Now that we know that the elf who was too busy taking elfies met Brave Dave on Sunday, we can deduce that the elf who wasn't mistletoeing the line must have met Brave Dave on Saturday.

Issue: Too busy taking elfies = Day: Sunday
Issue: Wasn't mistletoeing the line = Day: Saturday
Responsibility: Quizmas Committee = Day: Thursday

B. We know that the issues of taking elfies and not mistletoeing the line were discussed on Sunday and Saturday. Hence, the other issues must have been discussed on Monday, Tuesday, and Thursday. Clue 5 states that the lack of elf discipline was discussed earlier in the week than the lack of elf confidence. This means that the lack of elf discipline was discussed either on Monday or Tuesday, and the lack of elf confidence was discussed either on Tuesday or Thursday.

Clue 6 indicates that the need for elf improvement was discussed later in the week than when the meeting with the Elf and Safety Manager of the Elf Press took place. This is to say that the need for elf improvement must have taken place either on Tuesday or Thursday, and the meeting with the Elf and Safety Manager of the Elf Press must have taken place on Monday or Tuesday.

We have now established that the lack of elf discipline was discussed either on Monday or Tuesday, the lack of elf confidence was discussed either on Tuesday or Thursday, and the need for elf improvement was discussed either on Tuesday or Thursday. Since the lack of elf confidence and the need for elf improvement were discussed on Tuesday and Thursday (but not necessarily in this order), the lack of elf discipline must have been discussed on Monday.

Issue: Lacked elf discipline = Day: Monday
Issue: Lacked elf confidence = Day: Tuesday OR Thursday
Issue: Needed elf improvement = Day: Tuesday OR Thursday
Responsibility: Elf Press = Day: Monday OR Tuesday

C. Clue 2 states that Bearly Careless met Brave Dave the day before the elf who was in charge of the Excellent Elf School's safety procedures. When we look at the day options in the grid, we can see that there are only 2 potentially feasible options:

1. If Bearly Careless met Brave Dave on Monday, the elf in charge of the Excellent Elf School's safety procedures met Brave Dave on Tuesday.
2. If Bearly Careless met Brave Dave on Saturday, the elf in charge of the Excellent Elf School's safety procedures met Brave Dave on Sunday.

This is to say, Bearly Careless met Brave Dave either on Monday or Saturday, and the elf in charge of the Excellent Elf School's safety procedures met Brave Dave either on Tuesday or Sunday.

Elf: Bearly Careless = Day: Monday OR Saturday
Responsibility: Excellent Elf School = Day: Tuesday OR Sunday

D. We established in Explanation C that Bearly Careless met Brave Dave either on Monday or Saturday. We established in Explanation B that the elf who lacked elf discipline met Brave Dave on Monday and we established in Explanation A that the elf who wasn't mistletoeing the line met Brave Dave on Saturday. This is to say that if Bearly Careless met Brave Dave on Monday, they lacked elf discipline. If Bearly Careless met Brave Dave on Saturday, they weren't mistletoeing the line. Clue 7 indicates that Bearly Careless did not have an issue with mistletoeing the line. Therefore, Bearly Careless must have lacked elf discipline and met Brave Dave on Monday.

Elf	Responsibility	Issue	Day
Bearly Careless		Lacked elf discipline	Monday
Les Lawless			
Kinda Mindless			
Knot Reckless			
Teeny Thoughtless			

E. We established in Explanation C that the elf responsible for the Excellent Elf School's safety met Brave Dave the day after Bearly Careless and deduced that this would be either on Tuesday or Sunday. We now know that Bearly Careless met Brave Dave on Monday. Therefore, the elf responsible for the Excellent Elf School's safety met Brave Dave on Tuesday.

Responsibility: Excellent Elf School = Day: Tuesday

F. Clue 8 states that the 2 elves who both had a name with the 1st name and family name sharing the same initial letter were seen by Brave Dave 5 days apart. When we look at the elf names, we can see that the 2 elves in question must be Les Lawless and Teeny Thoughtless. So, these 2 elves met

Brave Dave 5 days apart. When we look at the day options in the grid, we can see that there are 2 potentially feasible options: Les Lawless and Teeny Thoughtless met Brave Dave on Monday and Saturday (but not necessarily in this order), or they met him on Tuesday and Sunday (but not necessarily in this order). However, we already know that Bearly Careless met Brave Dave on Monday. Therefore, Les Lawless and Teeny Thoughtless must have met Brave Dave on Tuesday and Sunday (but not necessarily in this order).

Elf: Les Lawless = Day: Tuesday OR Sunday
Elf: Teeny Thoughtless = Day: Tuesday OR Sunday

G. Clue 4 states that if Kinda Mindless was in no need of elf improvement, he met Brave Dave on Thursday, and if, instead Knot Reckless was seen by Brave Dave on the day after Les Lawless, Knot Reckless was the Elf and Safety Manager of the Reindeer Grooming Bureau. We know from Explanation F that Les Lawless met Brave Dave either on Tuesday or Sunday. For Knot Reckless to have met Brave Dave on the day after Les Lawless, Knot Reckless would have had to have met Brave Dave either on Wednesday or Monday. However, Wednesday is not a listed option in the grid. Also, the puzzle is about last week (as explained in the backstory) and, therefore, there is no option for Monday the following week. Furthermore, even if this weren't the case, Monday would not be feasible as it was Bearly Careless who met Brave Dave on Monday. Therefore, we can deduce that the statement about Knot Reckless meeting Brave Dave on the day after Les Lawless and being the Elf and Safety Manager of the Reindeer Grooming Bureau is not true. It follows from this that the 1st part of Clue 4 must be true: Kinda Mindless was in no need of elf improvement and he met Brave Dave on Thursday.

We established in Explanation B that the elves who either lacked elf confidence or needed elf improvement met Brave Dave on Tuesday and Thursday (but not necessarily in this order). We now know that Kinda Mindless met Brave Dave on Thursday and he was in no need of elf improvement. Therefore, he must have lacked elf confidence.

We should also note that Clue 4 refers to Kinda Mindless as male (he met Brave Dave on Thursday).

Kinda Mindless – This elf is male

Elf	Responsibility	Issue	Day
Bearly Careless		Lacked elf discipline	Monday
Les Lawless			
Kinda Mindless		Lacked elf confidence	Thursday
Knot Reckless			
Teeny Thoughtless			

H. We established in Explanation A that the elf who was responsible for the Quizmas Committee's safety met Brave Dave on Thursday. Since we now know that Kinda Mindless met Brave Dave on Thursday, we can deduce that Kinda Mindless was responsible for the Quizmas Committee's safety.

Elf	Responsibility	Issue	Day
Bearly Careless		Lacked elf discipline	Monday
Les Lawless			
Kinda Mindless	Quizmas Committee	Lacked elf confidence	Thursday
Knot Reckless			
Teeny Thoughtless			

I. We now know that Bearly Careless met Brave Dave on Monday and Kinda Mindless met him on Thursday. We established in Explanation F that Les Lawless and Teeny Thoughtless met Brave Dave on Tuesday and Sunday (but not necessarily in this order). It follows from this that Knot Reckless must have met Brave Dave on Saturday.

We established in Explanation A that the elf who met Brave Dave on Saturday wasn't mistletoeing the line. We now know that it was Knot Reckless who met Brave Dave on Saturday. Therefore, it was Knot Reckless who wasn't mistletoeing the line.

Elf	Responsibility	Issue	Day
Bearly Careless		Lacked elf discipline	Monday
Les Lawless			
Kinda Mindless	Quizmas Committee	Lacked elf confidence	Thursday
Knot Reckless		Wasn't mistletoeing the line	Saturday
Teeny Thoughtless			

J. Clue 7 states that Teeny Thoughtless and Bearly Careless were not involved in enforcing any safety procedures regarding reindeer grooming. This is to say that they weren't responsible for the Reindeer Grooming Bureau. We also know that Kinda Mindless was responsible for the Quizmas Committee, and therefore, cannot have been responsible for the Reindeer Grooming Bureau. Clue 4 states that if Knot Reckless was seen by Brave Dave on the day after Les Lawless, Knot Reckless was the Elf and Safety Manager of the Reindeer Grooming Bureau. We established in Explanation G that Knot Reckless was not seen on the day after Les Lawless. Therefore, Knot Reckless cannot have been the Elf and Safety Manager of the Reindeer Grooming Bureau. It follows from this that it must be Les Lawless who was responsible for the Reindeer Grooming Bureau.

Elf	Responsibility	Issue	Day
Bearly Careless		Lacked elf discipline	Monday
Les Lawless	Reindeer Grooming Bureau		
Kinda Mindless	Quizmas Committee	Lacked elf confidence	Thursday
Knot Reckless		Wasn't mistletoeing the line	Saturday
Teeny Thoughtless			

K. We established in Explanation E that the elf who was responsible for the Excellent Elf School's safety met Brave Dave on Tuesday. We established in Explanation F that it was either Les Lawless or Teeny Thoughtless who met Brave Dave on Tuesday, and that the other one met Brave Dave on Sunday. We now know that Les Lawless was responsible for the Reindeer Grooming Bureau. Therefore, Les Lawless cannot have met Brave Dave on Tuesday as this was the day when the elf who was responsible for the Excellent Elf School's safety met Brave Dave. It follows from this that it must have been Teeny Thoughtless who met Brave Dave on Tuesday and was responsible for the Excellent Elf School's safety.

We established in Explanation D that Les Lawless and Teeny Thoughtless met Brave Dave on Tuesday and Sunday (but not necessarily in this order). Since we now know that Teeny Thoughtless met Brave Dave on Tuesday, it must be Les Lawless who met Brave Dave on Sunday.

Elf	Responsibility	Issue	Day
Bearly Careless		Lacked elf discipline	Monday
Les Lawless	Reindeer Grooming Bureau		Sunday
Kinda Mindless	Quizmas Committee	Lacked elf confidence	Thursday
Knot Reckless		Wasn't mistletoeing the line	Saturday
Teeny Thoughtless	Excellent Elf School		Tuesday

L. We established in Explanation B that the elves who lacked elf confidence and needed elf improvement met Brave Dave on Tuesday or Thursday. We know that Kinda Mindless lacked elf confidence and met Brave Dave on Thursday. Therefore, the elf who needed elf improvement must have met Brave Dave on Tuesday. We know that it was Teeny Thoughtless who met Brave Dave on Tuesday. Therefore, it must have been Teeny Thoughtless who needed elf improvement.

We know that Bearly Careless lacked elf discipline, Kinda Mindless lacked elf confidence, Knot Reckless wasn't mistletoeing the line, and Teeny Thoughtless needed elf improvement. Therefore, it must be Les Lawless who was too busy taking elfies.

Elf	Responsibility	Issue	Day
Bearly Careless		Lacked elf discipline	Monday
Les Lawless	Reindeer Grooming Bureau	Too busy taking elfies	Sunday
Kinda Mindless	Quizmas Committee	Lacked elf confidence	Thursday
Knot Reckless		Wasn't mistletoeing the line	Saturday
Teeny Thoughtless	Excellent Elf School	Needed elf improvement	Tuesday

M. We established in Explanation B that the elf who was responsible for the Elf Press met Brave Dave either on Monday or Tuesday. We now know that Teeny Thoughtless, who was responsible for the Excellent Elf School, met Brave Dave on Tuesday. Therefore, the elf responsible for the Elf Press must have met Brave Dave on Monday. We know that it was Bearly Careless who met Brave Dave on Monday. Therefore, it must be Bearly Careless who was responsible for the Elf Press.

We know that Bearly Careless was responsible for the Elf Press, Les Lawless was responsible for the Reindeer Grooming Bureau, Kinda Mindless was responsible for the Quizmas Committee, and Teeny Thoughtless was responsible for the Excellent Elf School. Therefore, it must be Knot Reckless who was responsible for the Engineering Unit.

Elf	Responsibility	Issue	Day
Bearly Careless	Elf Press	Lacked elf discipline	Monday
Les Lawless	Reindeer Grooming Bureau	Too busy taking elfies	Sunday
Kinda Mindless	Quizmas Committee	Lacked elf confidence	Thursday
Knot Reckless	Engineering Unit	Wasn't mistletoeing the line	Saturday
Teeny Thoughtless	Excellent Elf School	Needed elf improvement	Tuesday

14. Stocking Thrillers

A. Clue 6 indicates that there were 3 teams whose stockings were adorned with stripes and these stockings were made with the help of a sewing machine and super glue. When we look at the picture, we can see that the 3 stockings with stripes are in Places 1, 2, and 5. Hence, these stockings were made with the help of a sewing machine and super glue. Clue 6 further indicates that there was a crocheted stocking and Clue 7 indicates that there was a knitted stocking. These stockings must have been in Places 3 and 4.

Place nos: 1, 2, and 5 = Stockings that were made with the help of a sewing machine and super glue
Place no: 3 = A stocking that was either knitted or crocheted
Place no: 4 = A stocking that was either knitted or crocheted

Clue 8 states that the team that used the most super glue placed their stocking between the beautifully crocheted stocking and the stocking that later found its way to Firling. We just established that the stockings for which super glue had been used were in Places 1, 2, and 5. Since the stockings in Places 1 and 5 are at the edges of the row, they cannot be the stocking which was placed between 2 other stockings – namely the one that was crocheted and the other which ended up in Firling. Therefore, the stocking in question must have been the stocking in Place 2. Of the stockings either side of the one in Place 2, one was in Place 1 and the other in Place 3. We established above that the crocheted stocking was either in Place 3 or 4. Since it was next to the stocking in Place 2, it must have been in Place 3. It follows from this that the stocking that ended up in Firling must have been in Place 1.

Since the knitted stocking and the crocheted stocking were in Places 3 and 4, and since we now know that the crocheted stocking was in Place 3, the knitted stocking must have been in Place 4.

Place no: 1 = Village: Firling
Place no: 2 = Stocking for which the most super glue had been used
Place no: 3 = Crocheted stocking
Place no: 4 = Knitted stocking

B. Clue 8 indicates that *Dr. Snow* was placed inside a stocking for which the elves had used the most super glue. We established in Explanation A that this stocking was in Place 2 in front of Santa's fireplace. Clue 2 indicates that *Dr. Snow* was found in Myrrhakesh. Therefore, it was the stocking in Place 2 that contained *Dr. Snow* and was found in Myrrhakesh.

Place no: 2 = Book: Dr. Snow = Village: Myrrhakesh

C. Clue 4 states that the sum of the place numbers of the 2 stockings in which *One Flew over the Yuletide Guest* and the book chosen by Naughty Nutcrackers were hidden was 2 numbers lower than the place number of the stocking that ended up in Sleigh-Jing. When we look at the place number options in the logic grid, we can see that the stocking that ended up in Sleigh-Jing must have been in Place 5: this is because for the sum of 2 other stockings' place numbers to be 2 numbers lower than 5 ($5 - 2 = 3$) is the lowest possible number that the sum of 2 other numbers can equal (that is, $1 + 2 = 3$). It follows from this that of the stocking that contained *One Flew over the Yuletide Guest* and the stocking made by Naughty Nutcrackers, one must have been in Place 1 and the other must have been in Place 2 (but not necessarily in this order).

However, we established in Explanation B that it was *Dr. Snow* that was found in Myrrhakesh and that it was in the stocking in Place 2. Therefore, *One Flew over the Yuletide Guest* must have been in the stocking in Place 1 and, consequently, the Naughty Nutcrackers' stocking must have been in Place 2. Furthermore, as established in Explanation B and mentioned earlier in this paragraph, *Dr. Snow* was in the stocking in Place 2 and ended up in Myrrhakesh. Therefore, *Dr. Snow* must have been the book that Naughty Nutcrackers chose and which they took to Myrrhakesh.

Book: One Flew over the Yuletide Guest = Place no: 1
Place no: 5 = Village: Sleigh-Jing

Team	Book	Place no.	Village
Jingle Jangles			
More Bells Than Whistles			
Naughty Nutcrackers	*Dr. Snow*	2	Myrrhakesh
Rudolph's Rebels			
Stocking Squad			

D. Clue 1 indicates that Stocking Squad and Jingle Jangles' stockings looked identical. When we look at the picture, we can see that the stockings in Places 1 and 5 look identical. Therefore, of Stocking Squad and Jingle Jangles, one's socking was in Place 1 and the other's stocking was in Place 5 (but not necessarily in this order).

Clue 9 indicates that Jingle Jangles took their stocking to a village whose name came alphabetically earlier than where the knitted stocking was taken. Clue 7 indicates that the knitted stocking ended up in Greenstown. Therefore, Jingle Jangles must have taken their stocking to either Budafest or Firling.

We established above that Jingle Jangles' stocking was either in Place 1 or 5. We established in Explanation A that the stocking in Place 1 ended up in Firling, and we established in Explanation C that the stocking in Place 5 ended up in Sleigh-Jing. Since Sleigh-Jing is not one of the options where Jingle Jangles could have taken their stocking but Firling is, we can deduce that Jingle Jangles' stocking must have been in Place 1 and their stocking must have ended up in Firling. It follows from this that Stocking Squad's stocking, which was in Place 5, must have been taken to Sleigh-Jing.

We established in Explanation C that *One Flew over the Yuletide Guest* was in the stocking in Place 1 in front of Santa's fireplace. We now know that Jingle Jangles' stocking was in Place 1. Therefore, it was Jingle Jangles who chose *One Flew over the Yuletide Guest*.

Knitted stocking = Village: Greenstown

Team	Book	Place no.	Village
Jingle Jangles	*One Flew over the Yuletide Guest*	1	Firling
More Bells Than Whistles			
Naughty Nutcrackers	*Dr. Snow*	2	Myrrhakesh
Rudolph's Rebels			
Stocking Squad		5	Sleigh-Jing

E. Clue 3 states that it was either *The Sleigh of Silence* or *Polar Jar* that was found by a little girl at the edge of a village green; and that if it was the

former, it was Rudolph's Rebels who deposited a stocking in Firling, but if it was the latter, this book had been placed inside a knitted stocking. We now know that it was Jingle Jangles who deposited a stocking in Firling, not Rudolph's Rebels. It follows from this that it cannot have been *The Sleigh of Silence* that was found by a little girl at the edge of a village green, but it was *Polar Jar* that the little girl found inside a knitted stocking.

We established in Explanation A that the knitted stocking was in Place 4 in front of Santa's fireplace, and we established in Explanation D that the knitted stocking was taken to Greenstown. Therefore, the little girl who found *Polar Jar* inside the knitted stocking was in Greenstown and, before this stocking got there, it was in Place 4 in front of Santa's fireplace.

Book: Polar Jar = Place no: 4 = Village: Greenstown

F. Clue 6 states that the crocheted stocking was closer to the decorative Christmas tree than the stocking that contained *The Hunt for Red Pullover*. We established in Explanation A that the crocheted stocking was in Place 3. Also, when we look at the picture, we can see that the decorative Christmas tree is on the left-hand side of the fireplace. Therefore, we can express Clue 6 as follows: the crocheted stocking in Place 3 was to the left of the stocking that contained *The Hunt for Red Pullover*. This means that *The Hunt for Red Pullover* must have been in a stocking that was in either Place 4 or 5. However, we established in Explanation E that *Polar Jar* was in the stocking in Place 4. Therefore, *The Hunt for Red Pullover* must have been in the stocking in Place 5. We know that the stocking in Place 5 was made by Stocking Squad. Therefore, *The Hunt for Red Pullover* must have been Stocking Squad's choice.

Team	Book	Place no.	Village
Jingle Jangles	*One Flew over the Yuletide Guest*	1	Firling
More Bells Than Whistles			
Naughty Nutcrackers	*Dr. Snow*	2	Myrrhakesh
Rudolph's Rebels			
Stocking Squad	*The Hunt for Red Pullover*	5	Sleigh-Jing

G. Clue 5 states that More Bells Than Whistles' stocking was farther right in front of Santa's fireplace than the stocking that ended up in Budafest. As More Bells Than Whistles' stocking is compared with the stocking that ended up in Budafest, we can deduce that these are 2 different stockings and, therefore, More Bells Than Whistles' stocking cannot have ended up in Budafest. Since Jingle Jangles' stocking ended up in Firling, Naughty Nutcrackers' stocking ended up in Myrrhakesh, and Stocking Squad's stocking ended up in Sleigh-Jing, the stocking that ended up in Budafest must have been Rudolph's Rebels' stocking. Consequently, the stocking that ended up in Greenstown must have been More Bells Than Whistles' stocking.

Team	Book	Place no.	Village
Jingle Jangles	*One Flew over the Yuletide Guest*	1	Firling
More Bells Than Whistles			Greenstown
Naughty Nutcrackers	*Dr. Snow*	2	Myrrhakesh
Rudolph's Rebels			Budafest
Stocking Squad	*The Hunt for Red Pullover*	5	Sleigh-Jing

H. We established in Explanation E that the stocking in Place 4 contained *Polar Jar* and ended up in Greenstown. We now know that More Bells Than Whistles' stocking ended up in Greenstown. Therefore, More Bells Than Whistles' stocking must have been in Place 4 and contained *Polar Jar*.

We now know that Jingle Jangles' stocking was in Place 1, More Bells Than Whistles' stocking was in Place 4, Naughty Nutcrackers' stocking was in Place 2, and Stocking Squad's stocking was in Place 5. Therefore, Rudolph's Rebels' stocking must have been in Place 3.

We now know that Jingle Jangles' stocking contained *One Flew over the Yuletide Guest*, More Bells Than Whistles' stocking contained *Polar Jar*, Naughty Nutcrackers' stocking contained *Dr. Snow*, and Stocking Squad's stocking contained *The Hunt for Red Pullover*. Therefore, Rudolph's Rebels' stocking must have contained *The Sleigh of Silence*.

Team	Book	Place no.	Village
Jingle Jangles	*One Flew over the Yuletide Guest*	1	Firling
More Bells Than Whistles	*Polar Jar*	4	Greenstown
Naughty Nutcrackers	*Dr. Snow*	2	Myrrhakesh
Rudolph's Rebels	*The Sleigh of Silence*	3	Budafest
Stocking Squad	*The Hunt for Red Pullover*	5	Sleigh-Jing

15. Merry Quizmas

A. Clue 1 indicates that Quizzly Bears wore polar bear costumes.

Clue 4 indicates that, unlike other teams, Les Quizerables and the team with the pinecone outfits helped each other design and sew their costumes. Clue 11 indicates that Quizmas Crackers had collaborated with the sewing experts in the Les Quizerables team. This means that Quizmas Crackers must be the team that wore the pinecone costumes.

Team	Question no.	Costume	Table no.
Hark the Herald Angels Win			
Les Quizerables			
Quizmas Crackers		Pinecones	
Quizzly Bears		Polar bears	
The Noel-It-Alls			

B. Clue 2 states that the team that sat closest to Santa's fireplace got the question relating to sharks wrong. When we look at Professor Quiz Whitty's index cards, we can see that Question 11 is about sharks (Who delivers presents to baby sharks? Santa Jaws.) Therefore, the team that sat closest to Santa's fireplace got Question 11 wrong.

Clue 11 indicates that Quizmas Crackers sat closest to the fireplace. Since the team that sat closest to Santa's fireplace got Question 11 wrong, it must be Quizmas Crackers who got Question 11 wrong.

Quizmas Crackers – Sat closest to the fireplace

Team	Question no.	Costume	Table no.
Hark the Herald Angels Win			
Les Quizerables			
Quizmas Crackers	11	Pinecones	
Quizzly Bears		Polar bears	
The Noel-It-Alls			

C. To solve the puzzle we need to work out how the different pictures were drawn on the question cards. Clue 5 indicates that the teddy bear was a pencil drawing. When we look at the question cards, we can see that Question 7 had a teddy bear on its card. Therefore, Question 7 is associated with the pencil drawing.

Clue 7 indicates that the moon was painted and the bauble was stencilled. When we look at the question cards, we can see that Question 9 had the moon on its card and Question 27 had a bauble on its card. Therefore, Question 9 is associated with a painted picture and Question 27 is associated with a stencilled picture.

Clue 8 indicates that there were 2 crayon drawings. Since we know how the 3 pictures on the question cards 7, 9, and 27 were created, we can deduce that Questions 11 and 18 – which depicted a candy cane and a wrapped candy respectively – were decorated with crayon drawings.

Question 7 = Teddy bear = Pencil
Question 9 = Moon = Painted
Question 11 = Candy cane = Crayon
Question 18 = Wrapped candy = Crayon
Question 27 = Bauble = Stencilled

D. Clue 4 indicates that the sum of Les Quizerable's table number and the table number of the team who wore pinecone outfits was 10 less than the sum of the question numbers they got wrong. We know that the team that wore the pinecone costumes was Quizmas Crackers. Therefore, we can express Clue 4 as follows: the sum of Les Quizerables and Quizmas Crackers' table numbers was 10 less than the sum of the question numbers they got wrong.

Clue 4 indicates that neither of these teams' incorrect question was on a card that had painted or stencilled pictures on them. We established in Explanation C that the painted moon was on question card 9 and the stencilled bauble was on question card 27. Therefore, neither team got Questions 9 or 27 wrong. Since we already know that Quizmas Crackers got Question 11 wrong, we can deduce that Les Quizerables must have got Question 7 or Question 18 wrong. Let's work out which one it might be.

If Les Quizerables got Question 18 wrong, and since Quizmas Crackers got Question 11 wrong, the sum of these numbers is 29. This would mean that for the sum of their table numbers to be 10 less, the sum of their table numbers would have to be 19. When we look at the table number options, we can see that there are no options that would give us the sum of 19.

If Les Quizerables got Question 7 wrong, and since Quizmas Crackers got Question 11 wrong, the sum of these numbers is 18. This would mean that for the sum of their table numbers to be 10 less, the sum of their table numbers would have to be 8. When we look at the table number options, we can see that the table numbers 3 and 5 would give us the sum of 8. So, we can now deduce that Les Quizerables must have got Question 7 wrong. It follows from this that, of Les Quizerables and Quizmas Crackers, one sat at Table 3 and the other at Table 5 (but not necessarily in this order).

Team: Les Quizerables = Table no: 3 OR 5
Team: Quizmas Crackers = Table no: 3 OR 5

Team	Question no.	Costume	Table no.
Hark the Herald Angels Win			
Les Quizerables	7		
Quizmas Crackers	11	Pinecones	
Quizzly Bears		Polar bears	
The Noel-It-Alls			

E. Clue 8 indicates that the teams who sat the closest to and the farthest from the fireplace got the 2 questions whose cards featured crayon drawings wrong. We established in Explanation C that the question cards with crayon pictures referred to Questions 11 and 18. We established in Explanation B that it was Quizmas Crackers who sat closest to the fireplace. Since we know that Quizmas Crackers got Question 11 wrong, it must be the team sitting the farthest from the fireplace that got Question 18 wrong.

Clue 8 further states that the sum of these 2 teams' table numbers was 13. We established in Explanation D that Quizmas Crackers' table number was either 3 or 5. When we look at the table number options in the grid, we can see that the only way the sum of these 2 teams' table numbers was 13 is if Quizmas Crackers' table number was 5 and the table number of the team who sat the farthest from the fireplace was 8.

Team sitting farthest from the fireplace = Question no: 18 = Table no: 8

Team	Question no.	Costume	Table no.
Hark the Herald Angels Win			
Les Quizerables	7		
Quizmas Crackers	11	Pinecones	5
Quizzly Bears		Polar bears	
The Noel-It-Alls			

F. We established in Explanation D that Les Quizerables sat at Table 3 or 5. We now know that it was Quizmas Crackers that sat at Table 5. Therefore, Les Quizerables must have sat at Table 3.

Team	Question no.	Costume	Table no.
Hark the Herald Angels Win			
Les Quizerables	7		3
Quizmas Crackers	11	Pinecones	5
Quizzly Bears		Polar bears	
The Noel-It-Alls			

G. Clue 10 states that The Noel-It-Alls wore either the snowball or the

Christmas pudding costumes, and that if they wore the former, they got the question relating to the gingerbread man wrong, but if they wore the latter, they sat at Table 6. When we look at the question cards, we can see that the question relating to the gingerbread man is Question 7 (Why shouldn't you mess with the gingerbread man? He's a tough cookie.) We know that it was Les Quizerables who got Question 7 wrong. Therefore, it cannot have been The Noel-It-Alls who got it wrong. It follows from this that The Noel-It-Alls must have worn the Christmas pudding costumes and they must have sat at Table 6.

Team	Question no.	Costume	Table no.
Hark the Herald Angels Win			
Les Quizerables	7		3
Quizmas Crackers	11	Pinecones	5
Quizzly Bears		Polar bears	
The Noel-It-Alls		Christmas puddings	6

H. Clue 2 indicates that the number of the question relating to sharks was lower than the sum of the table numbers of Hark the Herald Angels Win and the team dressed up as Christmas puddings. We established in Explanation B that the question relating to sharks was Question 11. We also know that the team that dressed up as Christmas puddings was The Noel-It-Alls. Therefore, we can rephase Clue 2 as follows: The sum of the table numbers of Hark the Herald Angels Win and The Noel-It-Alls was more than 11. We know that The Noel-It-Alls sat at Table 6. When we look at the table number options in the grid, we can see that No. 8 is the only option where the sum of these 2 table numbers is more than 11. Therefore, Hark the Herald Angels Win sat at Table 8.

Since Hark the Herald Angels Win sat at Table 8, Les Quizerables sat at Table 3, Quizmas Crackers sat at Table 5, and The Noel-It-Alls sat at Table 6, it must be Quizzly Bears who sat at Table 1.

Team	Question no.	Costume	Table no.
Hark the Herald Angels Win			8
Les Quizerables	7		3
Quizmas Crackers	11	Pinecones	5
Quizzly Bears		Polar bears	1
The Noel-It-Alls		Christmas puddings	6

I. We established in Explanation E that the team that was the farthest from the fireplace sat at Table 8 and got Question 18 wrong. We now know that Hark the Herald Angels Win sat at Table 8. Therefore, they must be the team that sat the farthest from the fireplace and got Question 18 wrong.

Clue 6 indicates that the team that sat the farthest from the fireplace wore penguin costumes. Since we know that Hark the Herald Angles Win was the team that sat the farthest from the fireplace, it must be them who wore the penguin costumes.

Since Hark the Herald Angels Win wore penguin costumes, Quizmas Crackers wore pinecone costumes, Quizzly Bears wore polar bear costumes, and The Noel-It-Alls wore Christmas pudding costumes, it must be Les Quizerables who wore snowball costumes.

Team	Question no.	Costume	Table no.
Hark the Herald Angels Win	18	Penguins	8
Les Quizerables	7	Snowballs	3
Quizmas Crackers	11	Pinecones	5
Quizzly Bears		Polar bears	1
The Noel-It-Alls		Christmas puddings	6

J. Clue 6 indicates that the trophy for the best costumes went to the team whose table number was 3 numbers lower that the table number of the team that got the most difficult question wrong. Clue 3 explains that Professor Quiz Whitty had organized the questions in a way that they got progressively more difficult as the Quizmas Quiz went on. Therefore, of the questions that the 5 winning teams got wrong, Question 27 was the most difficult one. We can, hence, rephrase the clue as follows: the trophy for the best costumes went to the team whose table number was 3 numbers lower that the table number of the team that got Question 27 wrong.

At the moment we don't know which team got Question 27 wrong. However, we know that Hark the Herald Angels Win got Question 18 wrong, Les Quizerables got Question 7 wrong, and Quizmas Crackers got Question 11 wrong. Therefore, it must be either Quizzly Bears or The Noel-It-Alls who got Question 27 wrong. We do, however, know these teams' table numbers. Quizzly Bears sat at Table 1 and The Noel-It-Alls sat at Table 6. Since the trophy for the best costume went to the team whose table number was 3 lower than that team that got Question 27 wrong, the latter team cannot have been the one that sat at Table 1. Therefore, this team that got Question 27 wrong must have been the team that sat at Table 6 – which we know is The Noel-It-Alls – and the team that won the trophy for the best costume must have sat at Table 3 – which we know is Les Quizerables.

Since Hark the Herald Angels Win got Question 18 wrong, Les Quizerables got Question 7 wrong, Quizmas Crackers got Question 11 wrong, and The Noel-It-Alls got Question 27 wrong, it must be Quizzly Bears who got Question 9 wrong.

Team	Question no.	Costume	Table no.
Hark the Herald Angels Win	18	Penguins	8
Les Quizerables	7	Snowballs	3
Quizmas Crackers	11	Pinecones	5
Quizzly Bears	9	Polar bears	1
The Noel-It-Alls	27	Christmas puddings	6

16. Up to Snow Good

A. Clue 1 states that the snowball fight started 1 min after the lunchtime bells jingled and that it was 2 mins after the snowball fight's start time that Professor Quiz Whitty was hit. This is to say that Professor Quiz Whitty was hit 3 mins after the lunchtime bells jingled. Clue 7 indicates that the lunchtime bells jingled either at 1 pm (i.e. 13:00) or 13:01. If the lunchtime bells jingled at 13:00, Professor Quiz Whitty would have been hit at 13:03. If, instead, the lunchtime bells jingled at 13:01, Professor Quiz Whitty would have been hit at 13:04. Since the option of 13:04 does not exist in the logic puzzle grid, Professor Quiz Whitty must have been hit at 13:03.

Clue 6 indicates that Professor Quiz Whitty's disciplinary action involved saluting reindeer. Since Clue 2 explains that each person who was hit decided what the disciplinary action should be for the elf whose snowball had walloped them, this means that the elf who hit Professor Quiz Whitty with a snowball would have been required to salute reindeer.

Hit by snowball: Professor Quiz Whitty = Time: 13:03 = Consequence: Saluting reindeer
Lunchtime bells jingled at 13:00

B. Clue 7 states that if the lunchtime bells jingled at 1 pm (i.e. 13:00), it was Carol Winger who was asked to do a good deed, and if, instead, the lunchtime bells jingled at 13:01, it was Angie Near who was hit at 13:11. We established in Explanation A that the lunchtime bells jingled at 13:00. Therefore, Carol Winger was asked to do a good deed. And since the lunchtime bells didn't jingle at 13:01, Angie Near was not hit at 13:11.

Hit by snowball: Angie Near = Time: NOT 13:11

Elf	Hit by snowball	Time	Consequence
Carol Bringer			
Carol Slinger			
Carol Springer			
Carol Swinger			
Carol Winger			Good deed

C. Clue 5 states that Carol Springer's snowball hit an elf 2 mins earlier than when a snowball hit Angie Near. When we look at the time options, we can see that there are 2 potential combinations:

1. If Carol Springer's snowball hit an elf at 13:07, Angie Near would have been hit at 13:09.
2. If Carol Springer's snowball hit an elf at 13:09, Angie Near would have been hit at 13:11.

We established in Explanation B that Angie Near was not hit at 13:11. It follows from this that Carol Springer's snowball must have hit an elf at 13:07, and Angie Near must have been hit at 13:09.

Hit by snowball: Angie Near = Time: 13:09

Elf	Hit by snowball	Time	Consequence
Carol Bringer			
Carol Slinger			
Carol Springer		13:07	
Carol Swinger			
Carol Winger			Good deed

D. Clue 8 indicates that Aretha Holly was hit by a snowball earlier than the elves who made the snowball throwers miss watching the northern lights and do target practice. Clue 2 indicates that missing watching the northern lights was the consequence of an early bedtime. Therefore, we can rephrase Clue 8 as follows: Aretha Holly was hit by a snowball earlier than the elves who made the snowball throwers go to bed early and do target practice. This is to say that Aretha Holly's disciplinary action was neither sending anyone to bed early nor target practice. Also, we established in Explanation A that Professor Quiz Whitty's disciplinary action was saluting reindeer. Therefore, Aretha Holly's disciplinary action also cannot have been saluting reindeer. If follows from this that Aretha Holly's disciplinary action must have been either an elf talk in front of a mirror or a good deed.

Hit by snowball: Aretha Holly = Consequence: Elf talk in front of mirror OR Good deed

E. We established in Explanation A that Professor Quiz Whitty was hit by a snowball at 13:03. We established in Explanation D that Aretha Holly was hit by a snowball earlier than the elves who made the snowball throwers go to bed early and to do target practice. This is to say that there were at least 2 elves who were hit by snowballs after Aretha Holly, and there was 1 elf – Professor Quiz Whitty – who was hit by a snowball at 13:03. It follows from this that Aretha Holly cannot have been hit at 13:03 and there would have to be at least 2 elves that were hit by snowballs after her – i.e. the 2 elves who ordered the snowball throwers go to bed early and to do target practice. It follows from this that there are 2 potential options for when Aretha Holly could have been hit by a snowball:

1. If Aretha Holly was hit at 13:06, the 2 elves who ordered the snowball throwers go to bed early and to do target practice would have been hit at 2 out of the following 3 times; 13:07, 13:09, or 13:11 (but not necessarily in this order).
2. If Aretha Holly was hit at 13:07, the 2 elves who ordered the snowball throwers go to bed early and to do target practice would have been hit at 13:09 and 13:11 (but not necessarily in this order).

This is to say that Aretha Holly was hit either at 13:06 or 13:07. We can also deduce that neither of the 2 elves who ordered the snowball throwers go to bed early and to do target practice got hit at 13:06.

Hit by snowball: Aretha Holly = Time: 13:06 OR 13:07
Time: 13:06 = Consequence: NEITHER Early bedtime NOR Target practice

F. Clue 3 states that of the 2 elves who were hit by snowballs at the Excellent Elf School's entrance, the one who was hit later told the snowball thrower to stand in front of a mirror and give herself a good elf talk. Clue 4 indicates that Miss Tress was one of the elves hit by a snowball at the Excellent Elf School's entrance as she was coming out of the building. Clue 5 indicates that Carol Springer hit an elf who was just about to enter the Excellent Elf School. This means that Carol Springer cannot have hit Miss Tress (because Miss Tress was coming out of the building and the elf hit by Carol Springer was going into the building), but it must have been another elf. We know that Carol Springer's snowball hit an elf at 13:07, Professor Quiz Whitty was hit by a snowball at 13:03 (Explanation A), and Angie Near was hit by a snowball at 13:09 (Explanation C). Therefore, we can deduce that Carol Springer must have hit either Aretha Holly or Brave Dave at 13:07. It follows from this that Miss Tress must have been hit by a snowball either at 13:06 or 13:11.

As mentioned above, Clue 3 states that of the 2 elves who were hit by snowballs at the Excellent Elf School's entrance, the one who was hit later told the snowball thrower to stand in front of a mirror and give herself a good elf talk. Since we know that Carol Springer's snowball hit Aretha Holly or Brave at 13:07 and Miss Tress was hit by a snowball either at 13:06 or 13:11, there are 2 potential options for the time of being hit for which the consequence was an elf talk in front of a mirror:

1. If Miss Tress was hit by a snowball at 13:06, and Carol Springer's snowball hit Aretha Holly or Brave Dave at 13:07, it would have been Carol Springer

whose snowball hit an unintended target outside the school later, and therefore, she would have been told to have an elf talk in front of a mirror.
2. If Miss Tress was hit by a snowball at 13:11, and Carol Springer's snowball hit Aretha Holly or Brave Dave at 13:07, it would have been the elf whose snowball hit Miss Tress outside the school that happened later, and therefore, Miss Tress would have told the snowball thrower to have an elf talk in front of a mirror.

In either case, the elf hit by a snowball at 13:06 cannot have been the one telling the snowball thrower to give herself a good elf talk in front of a mirror.

We established in Explanation E that the consequence of being hit by a snowball at 13:06 was neither early bedtime nor target practice. We established in Explanation A that the consequence of begin hit by a snowball at 13:03 was saluting reindeer. Therefore, saluting reindeer cannot have been the consequence of being hit by a snowball at 13:06. Since we also know that an elf talk in front of a mirror cannot have been the consequence for the snowball thrower who hit an unintended target at 13:06, it follows that the consequence of being hit by a snowball at 13:06 was a good deed.

We know that it was Carol Winger who was told to do a good deed. Therefore, it must be Carol Winger whose snowball hit an unintended target at 13:06.

Elves hit by snowballs at the Excellent Elf School's entrance: Miss Tress AND Carol Springer's unintended target
Elf: Carol Springer = Hit by snowball: Aretha Holly OR Brave Dave
Hit by snowball: Miss Tress = Time: 13:06 or 13:11

Elf	Hit by snowball	Time	Consequence
Carol Bringer			
Carol Slinger			
Carol Springer		13:07	
Carol Swinger			
Carol Winger		13:06	Good deed

G. Clue 2 states that of the 2 elves whose snowballs landed on unintended targets 1 min apart, one of them was told to go to bed early. When we look at the time options, we can see that these times are 13:06 and 13:07 as they are the only times that are 1 min apart. We know that it was Carol Winger's snowball that hit an unintended target at 13:06 and Carol Springer's snowball that hit an unintended target at 13:07. Since we know that Carol Winger was asked to do a good deed, it must be Carol Springer who was told to go to bed early.

Elf	Hit by snowball	Time	Consequence
Carol Bringer			
Carol Slinger			
Carol Springer		13:07	Early bedtime
Carol Swinger			
Carol Winger		13:06	Good deed

H. We established in Explanation E that Aretha Holly was hit by a snowball either at 13:06 or 13:07. We know that Carol Springer's snowball hit an unintended target at 13:07 and Carol Winger's snowball hit an unintended target at 13:06. Therefore, it was either Carol Springer or Carol Winger whose snowball hit Aretha Holly.

We established in Explanation D that Aretha Holly told the snowball thrower either to have an elf talk in front of a mirror or to do a good deed. We know that Carol Springer was told to go to bed early and Carol Winger was told to do a good deed. It follows from this that Aretha Holly must have told the snowball thrower to do a good deed. Therefore, it was Carol Winger whose snowball hit Aretha Holly.

Elf	Hit by snowball	Time	Consequence
Carol Bringer			
Carol Slinger			
Carol Springer		13:07	Early bedtime
Carol Swinger			
Carol Winger	Aretha Holly	13:06	Good deed

I. We established in Explanation F that Carol Springer's snowball hit either Aretha Holly or Brave Dave. We now know that it was Carol Winger whose snowball hit Aretha Holly. Therefore, Carol Springer's snowball must have hit Brave Dave.

Elf	Hit by snowball	Time	Consequence
Carol Bringer			
Carol Slinger			
Carol Springer	Brave Dave	13:07	Early bedtime
Carol Swinger			
Carol Winger	Aretha Holly	13:06	Good deed

J. We established in Explanation F that Miss Tress was hit by a snowball either at 13:06 or 13:11. We now know that it was Aretha Holly who was hit at 13:06. Therefore, Miss Tress must have been hit by a snowball at 13:11.

We established in Explanation F (Option 2) that if Miss Tress was hit by a snowball at 13:11, and Carol Springer's snowball hit an elf at 13:07, it would have been Miss Tress who told the snowball thrower to have an elf talk in front of a mirror.

Hit by snowball: Miss Tress = Time: 13:11 = Consequence: Elf talk in front mirror

K. Clue 6 indicates that Carol Bringer hit a passer-by on her back. Clue 4 indicates that Miss Tress was hit on her forehead. Therefore, Carol Bringer cannot have been the elf whose snowball hit Miss Tress. Clue 2 indicates that Carol Swinger's snowball hit an unintended target earlier than the elf who was at the receiving end of a snowball behind Santa's workshop. This means that Carol Swinger's unintended target cannot have been the last one hit during the snowball fight. In other words, Carol Swinger's snowball cannot have hit Miss Tress – whom we know was hit last at 13:11 (Explanation J). It follows from this that Miss Tress must have been hit by Carol Slinger's snowball. We established in Explanation J that Miss Tress was hit at 13:11 and she told the snowball thrower to give herself an elf talk in front of a mirror.

Elf	Hit by snowball	Time	Consequence
Carol Bringer			
Carol Slinger	Miss Tress	13:11	Elf talk in front of mirror
Carol Springer	Brave Dave	13:07	Early bedtime
Carol Swinger			
Carol Winger	Aretha Holly	13:06	Good deed

L. We established in Explanation A that Professor Quiz Whitty was hit by a snowball at 13:03 and he told the snowball thrower to salute reindeer. We now know that Carol Slinger's snowball hit Miss Tress, Carol Springer's snowball hit Brave Dave, and Carol Winger's snowball hit Aretha Holly. It follows from this that Professor Quiz Whitty cannot have been the unintended target of Carol Slinger, Carol Springer, or Carol Winger. Hence, it must be either Carol Bringer or Carol Swinger whose snowball hit him. Clue 6 states that Carol Bringer was not the recipient of Professor Quiz Whitty's disciplinary action. Therefore, she cannot have been the one whose snowball hit Professor Quiz Whitty. It follows from this that it must be Carol Swinger whose snowball hit Professor Quiz Whitty at 13:03 and she was told to salute reindeer as a consequence.

Elf	Hit by snowball	Time	Consequence
Carol Bringer			
Carol Slinger	Miss Tress	13:11	Elf talk in front of mirror
Carol Springer	Brave Dave	13:07	Early bedtime
Carol Swinger	Professor Quiz Whitty	13:03	Saluting reindeer
Carol Winger	Aretha Holly	13:06	Good deed

M. We know that Carol Slinger's snowball hit Miss Tress, Carol Springer's snowball hit Brave Dave, Carol Swinger's snowball hit Professor Quiz Whitty, and Carol Winger's snowball hit Aretha Holly. Therefore, Carol Bringer's unintended target must have been Angie Near.

We know the times when the snowballs of Carol Slinger, Carol Springer, Carol Swinger, and Carol Winger hit their unintended targets: 13:11, 13:07, 13:03, and 13:06 respectively. It follows from this that Carol Bringer's snowball must have hit an unintended target at 13:09.

We know that Carol Slinger was told to give herself an elf talk in front of a mirror, Carol Springer was told to go to bed early, Carol Swinger was told to salute reindeer, and Carol Winger was told to do a good deed. Therefore, it

must have been Carol Bringer who was told to do target practice.

Elf	Hit by snowball	Time	Consequence
Carol Bringer	Angie Near	13:09	Target practice
Carol Slinger	Miss Tress	13:11	Elf talk in front of mirror
Carol Springer	Brave Dave	13:07	Early bedtime
Carol Swinger	Professor Quiz Whitty	13:03	Saluting reindeer
Carol Winger	Aretha Holly	13:06	Good deed

17. Letter Safe than Sorry

A. Clue 8 states that Don Keigh's letter arrived earlier than the letter from Candle County. This means that Don Keigh's letter cannot have arrived on Friday. Clue 4 states that it was either Jay Walker or Joe King whose letter was posted on Monday. Clue 2 explains that it took 2 days for letters to arrive. Therefore, it was either Jay Walker or Joe King's letter that arrived on Wednesday. This means that the letter from Don Keigh cannot have arrived on Wednesday.

Clue 5 states that Don Keigh sent his letter to Santa on the same day as when the letter that said, "Dear Santa, the elves did it." was received. Clue 2 explains that it took 2 days for letters to arrive. Therefore, Don Keigh's letter would have arrived 2 days later than the letter that said, "Dear Santa, the elves did it." We established above that Don Keigh's letter cannot have arrived on Wednesday or Friday. When we look at the arrival day options, there's only 1 combination that is possible: The letter that said, "Dear Santa, the elves did it." must have arrived on Tuesday, and Don Keigh's letter – which arrived 2 days later – must have arrived on Thursday.

As mentioned above, Clue 8 states that Don Keigh's letter arrived earlier than the letter from Candle County. We now know that Don Keigh's letter arrived on Thursday. Therefore, the letter from Candle County must have arrived on Friday.

Name: Jay Walker OR Joe King = Arrival day: Wednesday
Dear Santa…: the elves did it = Arrival day: Tuesday
Location: Candle County = Arrival day: Friday

Name	Dear Santa…	Location	Arrival day
Dinah Mite			
Don Keigh			Thursday
Jay Walker			
Joe King			
Kay Oss			

B. Clue 5 indicates that the letter that said, "Dear Santa, the elves did it." was sent from Nutcracker Nook. We established in Explanation A that the letter that said, "Dear Santa, the elves did it." arrived on Tuesday. Therefore, this letter was sent from Nutcracker Nook.

Dear Santa…: the elves did it = Location: Nutcracker Nook = Arrival day: Tuesday

C. Clue 3 states that the letter from Hot Chocolate Hill arrived 1 day earlier than when the letter that said, "Dear Santa, I hope Rudolph eats the naughty list." was put in the Elf Mail. Clue 2 explains that it took 2 days for letters to arrive. This means that on one day the letter from Hot Chocolate Hill arrived, then the following day the letter that said, "Dear Santa, I hope Rudolph eats the naughty list." was posted, and 2 days later this letter arrived. It other words, the letter that said, "Dear Santa, I hope Rudolph eats the naughty list." arrived 3 days later than the letter from Hot Chocolate Hill. When we look at the arrival day options, there are 2 possibilities for how this combination can be true:

1. If the letter from Hot Chocolate Hill arrived on Monday, the letter that said, "Dear Santa, I hope Rudolph eats the naughty list." arrived on Thursday.

2. If the letter from Hot Chocolate Hill arrived on Tuesday, the letter that said, "Dear Santa, I hope Rudolph eats the naughty list." arrived on Friday.

We established in Explanation B that the letter from Nutcracker Nook arrived on Tuesday. Therefore, the letter from Hot Chocolate Hill cannot have arrived on Tuesday and must have arrived on Monday. Consequently, the letter that said, "Dear Santa, I hope Rudolph eats the naughty list." must have arrived on Thursday.

We know that it was Don Keigh's letter that arrived on Thursday. Therefore, it must be Don Keigh who wrote, "Dear Santa, I hope Rudolph eats the naughty list."

Location: Hot Chocolate Hill = Arrival day: Monday

Name	Dear Santa...	Location	Arrival day
Dinah Mite			
Don Keigh	I hope Rudolph eats the naughty list		Thursday
Jay Walker			
Joe King			
Kay Oss			

D. Clue 3 indicates that of the letter from Hot Chocolate Hill and the letter that said, "Dear Santa, I hope Rudolph eats the naughty list.", one of these letter writers had the letter O in their 1st name and the other in their last name. We know that the writer who said "Dear Santa, I hope Rudolph eats the naughty list." was Don Keigh – in other words, a person who had the letter O in their 1st name. Therefore, the person who posted a letter from Hot Chocolate Hill must have been someone with the letter O in their last name. When we look at the name options, there's only 1 person with the letter O in their last name: Kay Oss. Therefore, it was Kay Oss who sent a letter from Hot Chocolate Hill.

We established in Explanation C that that the letter that came from Hot Chocolate Hill arrived on Monday. Since we now know that it was Kay Oss who sent a letter from Hot Chocolate Hill, it is her letter that arrived on Monday.

Name	Dear Santa...	Location	Arrival day
Dinah Mite			
Don Keigh	I hope Rudolph eats the naughty list		Thursday
Jay Walker			
Joe King			
Kay Oss		Hot Chocolate Hill	Monday

E. Clue 7 indicates that Dinah Mite put her letter in the Elf Mail higher up on Ear Fell than where the letter that arrived on Monday came from. We know that the letter that arrived on Monday was Kay Oss' letter and it was posted in Hot Chocolate Hill. This means that Dinah Mite's letter was posted higher up than Hot Chocolate Hill. Clue 1 explains that the locations dotted along the road to the top of Ear Fell followed a reverse alphabetical order starting from Zest Zone's lowest altitude location to the highest peak called Angel Apex. For Dinah Mite's location to be higher up than Hot Chocolate Hill, it has to come alphabetically earlier than Hot Chocolate Hill. There is only 1 location in the location option list that fulfils this criterion: Candle County. Therefore, Dinah Mite's location was Candle County.

We established in Explanation A that the letter from Candle County arrived on Friday. Since Dinah Mite's letter was from Candle County, it was Dinah Mite's letter that arrived on Friday.

Name	Dear Santa...	Location	Arrival day
Dinah Mite		Candle County	Friday
Don Keigh	I hope Rudolph eats the naughty list		Thursday
Jay Walker			
Joe King			
Kay Oss		Hot Chocolate Hill	Monday

F. Clue 6 states that the letter from Sugarplum Station arrived 1 day later than the letter saying, "Dear Santa, I can explain." We know that the letter from Candle County arrived on Friday and the letter from Hot Chocolate Hill arrived on Monday. Therefore, the letter from Sugarplum Station cannot have arrived either on Friday or Monday. Also, we established in Explanation B that the letter from Nutcracker Nook arrived on Tuesday. Hence, the letter from Sugarplum Station cannot have arrived on Tuesday either. It follows from this that it must have arrived either on Wednesday or Thursday.

For the letter from Sugarplum Station to arrive 1 day later than the letter saying, "Dear Santa, I can explain.", there are 2 options that are potentially feasible:

1. If the letter from Sugarplum Station arrived on Wednesday, the letter that said, "Dear Santa, I can explain." would have arrived on Tuesday.
2. If the letter from Sugarplum Station arrived on Thursday, the letter that said, "Dear Santa, I can explain." would have arrived on Wednesday.

We established in Explanation A that the letter that arrived on Tuesday said, "Dear Santa, the elves did it." Therefore, the letter that said, "Dear Santa, I can explain." cannot have arrived on Tuesday, and must have arrived on Wednesday. It follows from this that the letter from Sugarplum Station must have arrived on Thursday.

We know that Don Keigh's letter arrived on Thursday. Therefore, it must be Don Keigh who posted the letter from Sugarplum Station.

Dear Santa...: I can explain = Arrival day: Wednesday

Name	Dear Santa...	Location	Arrival day
Dinah Mite		Candle County	Friday
Don Keigh	I hope Rudolph eats the naughty list	Sugarplum Station	Thursday
Jay Walker			
Joe King			
Kay Oss		Hot Chocolate Hill	Monday

G. We established in Explanation A that the letter that arrived on Tuesday said, "Dear Santa, the elves did it." and in Explanation F that the letter that arrived on Wednesday said, "Dear Santa, I can explain." Since Dinah Mite's letter arrived on Friday, these 2 letters cannot have been from her. Also, we know that Don Keigh wrote, "Dear Santa, I hope Rudolph eats the naughty list." Hence, this letter cannot have been Dinah Mite's letter either. Furthermore, Clue 7 states that Dinah Mite didn't write, "Dear Santa, please define nice." It follows from this that Dinah Mite must have written, "Dear Santa, is it too late now to say sorry?"

Name	Dear Santa...	Location	Arrival day
Dinah Mite	is it too late now to say sorry	Candle County	Friday
Don Keigh	I hope Rudolph eats the naughty list	Sugarplum Station	Thursday
Jay Walker			
Joe King			
Kay Oss		Hot Chocolate Hill	Monday

H. Clue 4 states that it was either Jay Walker or Joe King whose letter was posted on Monday, and that if it was Jay Walker's letter, he sent it from a place lower down on Ear Fell than Plum Pudding Place; if, instead it was Joe King's letter, he wrote, "Dear Santa, is it too late now to say sorry?" We now know that it was Dinah Mite who wrote, "Dear Santa, is it too late now to say sorry?" Therefore, it cannot have been Joe King, and must have been Jay Walker whose letter was posted on Monday.

We established in Explanation A that the letter that was posted on Monday by either Jay Walker or Joe King arrived on Wednesday – which we now know was the letter from Jay Walker. As mentioned above, Clue 4 states that if this letter was Jay Walker's letter, he sent it from a place lower down on Ear Fell than Plum Pudding Place. Clue 1 explains that the locations dotted along the road to the top of Ear Fell followed a reverse alphabetical order starting from Zest Zone's lowest altitude location to the highest peak called Angel Apex. For Jay Walker's location to be lower down than Plum Pudding Place, it has to come alphabetically later than Plum Pudding Place. There are only 2 locations in the location option list that fulfil this criterion: Sugarplum Station and Toboggan Town. Since Don Keigh sent a letter from Sugarplum Station, it must Toboggan Town from where Jay Walker sent a letter.

We established in Explanation F that the letter that arrived on Wednesday said, "Dear Santa, I can explain." We now know that it was Jay Walker's letter that arrived on Wednesday. Therefore, it was Jay Walker who wrote, "Dear Santa, I can explain."

Name	Dear Santa...	Location	Arrival day
Dinah Mite	is it too late now to say sorry	Candle County	Friday
Don Keigh	I hope Rudolph eats the naughty list	Sugarplum Station	Thursday
Jay Walker	I can explain	Toboggan Town	Wednesday
Joe King			
Kay Oss		Hot Chocolate Hill	Monday

I. We know that Dinah Mite's letter came from Candle County, Don Keigh's letter came from Sugarplum Station, Jay Walker's letter came from Toboggan Town, and Kay Oss' letter came from Hot Chocolate Hill. Therefore, it must be Joe King's letter that came from Nutcracker Nook.

We established in Explanation B that the letter that came from Nutcracker Nook arrived on Tuesday and said, "Dear Santa, the elves did it." Since we know that Joe King's letter came from Nutcracker Nook, it was his letter that arrived on Tuesday and said, "Dear Santa, the elves did it."

We know that Dinah Mite wrote, "Dear Santa, is it too late now to say sorry?", Don Keigh wrote, "Dear Santa, I hope Rudolph eats the naughty list.", Jay Walker wrote, "Dear Santa, I can explain.", and Joe King wrote, "Dear Santa, the elves did it." Therefore, it must be Kay Oss who wrote, "Dear Santa, please define nice."

Name	Dear Santa...	Location	Arrival day
Dinah Mite	is it too late now to say sorry	Candle County	Friday
Don Keigh	I hope Rudolph eats the naughty list	Sugarplum Station	Thursday
Jay Walker	I can explain	Toboggan Town	Wednesday
Joe King	the elves did it	Nutcracker Nook	Tuesday
Kay Oss	please define nice	Hot Chocolate Hill	Monday

18. Candle with Care

A. Clue 8 indicates that the 2 candles with an animal theme were in positions whose numbers equalled 6 when summed. Clue 2 states that *Santa Claws* depicted a stalking cat and Clue 6 describes *Bah-Hum-Pug* as a cute pug dog. Therefore, it is *Santa Claws* and *Bah-Hum-Pug* that were the candles with an animal theme. It is, then, their position numbers that equalled 6 when added together. When we look at the position number options, we can see that there are 2 potential combinations:

1. Of *Santa Claws* and *Bah-Hum-Pug*, one was in Position 1 and the other in Position 5 (but not necessarily in this order).
2. Of *Santa Claws* and *Bah-Hum-Pug*, one was in Position 2 and the other in Position 4 (but not necessarily in this order).

Clue 8 also indicates that the sum of the position numbers of the candles that incorporated elves in their designs was also 6. Clue 5 describes *Love You Snow Much* as depicting 2 infatuated elves holding hands, and Clue 7 describes *Christmas Tree Hugger* as a Christmas tree being hugged by a little elf. Hence, it is *Love You Snow Much* and *Christmas Tree Hugger* that were the candles that incorporated elves in their design. It is, then, their position numbers that equalled 6 when summed. When we look at the position number options, we can see that there are 2 potential combinations:

1. Of *Love You Snow Much* and *Christmas Tree Hugger,* one was in Position 1 and the other in Position 5 (but not necessarily in this order).
2. Of *Love You Snow Much* and *Christmas Tree Hugger,* one was in Position 2 and the other in Position 4 (but not necessarily in this order).

We can now deduce that *Santa Claws, Bah-Hum-Pug, Love You Snow Much,* and *Christmas Tree Hugger* cannot have been in Position 3. Therefore, it must be *Whisking You a Merry Christmas* (which Clue 3 describes as a candle in a shape of a large whisk standing upright in a mixing bowl) that was in Position 3.

Candle names: Bah-Hum-Pug and Santa Claws = Position: 1 and 5 OR 2 and 4 (but not necessarily in this order)
Candle names: Christmas Tree Hugger and Love You Snow Much = Position: 1 and 5 OR 2 and 4 (but not necessarily in this order)

Candle name	Ice lantern	Burning time	Position
Bah-Hum-Pug			
Christmas Tree Hugger			
Love You Snow Much			
Santa Claws			
Whisking You a Merry Christmas			3

B. Clue 8 states that the 2 candles with an animal theme were placed inside the cube and pyramid ice lanterns. We established in Explanation A that these candles were *Bah-Hum-Pug* and *Santa Claws*. Therefore, it was *Bah-Hum-Pug* and *Santa Claws* that were placed inside the cube and pyramid ice lanterns. Clue 6 indicates that *Bah-Hum-Pug* was positioned closer to the Excellent Elf School than the candle that was in the pyramid-shaped lantern. This is to say that *Bah-Hum-Pug* cannot have been in the pyramid-shaped lantern. It follows from this that *Bah-Hum-Pug* must have been in the cube-shaped lantern. Consequently, *Santa Claws* must have been in the pyramid-shaped ice lantern.

As mentioned above, Clue 6 indicates that *Bah-Hum-Pug* was positioned closer to the Excellent Elf School than the candle that was in the pyramid-shaped lantern. Now that we know that it was *Santa Claws* that was inside the pyramid-shaped lantern, we can rephrase the clue as follows: *Bah-Hum-Pug* was closer to the Excellent Elf School than *Santa Claws*. Clue 1 explains that the Excellent Elf School was in the west and Santa's workshop was in the east. Therefore, *Bah-Hum-Pug* was west of *Santa Claws*.

We established in Explanation A that there were 2 potential combinations in terms of where *Bah-Hum-Pug* and *Santa Claws* were positioned:

1. Of *Santa Claws* and *Bah-Hum-Pug*, one was in Position 1 and the other in Position 5 (but not necessarily in this order).
2. Of *Santa Claws* and *Bah-Hum-Pug*, one was in Position 2 and the other in Position 4 (but not necessarily in this order).

Since *Bah-Hum-Pug* was west of *Santa Claws*, it was either in Position 1 or 2, and *Santa Claws'* respective position was either in 4 or 5.

Candle name: Bah-Hum-Pug = Position: 1 OR 2
Candle name: Santa Claws = Position: 4 OR 5

Candle name	Ice lantern	Burning time	Position
Bah-Hum-Pug	Cube		
Christmas Tree Hugger			
Love You Snow Much			
Santa Claws	Pyramid		
Whisking You a Merry Christmas			3

C. Clue 7 states that if *Christmas Tree Hugger* didn't fit inside its ice lantern, it was in Position 5, and if, instead, it did fit inside a sphere-shaped ice lantern, it was in Position 3. We know that it was *Whisking You a Merry Christmas* that was in Position 3. Therefore, *Christmas Tree Hugger* cannot have been in Position 3. It follows from this that it must have been the candle that didn't fit inside its ice lantern and was in Position 5.

We established in Explanation A that if either *Love You Snow Much* or *Christmas Tree Hugger* was in Position 5, the other would be in Position 1. Since we now know that *Christmas Tree Hugger* was in Position 5, *Love You Snow Much* must have been in Position 1.

Christmas Tree Hugger = Did not fit inside its ice lantern

Candle name	Ice lantern	Burning time	Position
Bah-Hum-Pug	Cube		
Christmas Tree Hugger			5
Love You Snow Much			1
Santa Claws	Pyramid		
Whisking You a Merry Christmas			3

D. We established in Explanation B that *Bah-Hum-Pug* was either in Position 1 or 2. Since we know that *Love You Snow Much* was in Position 1, *Bah-Hum-Pug* must have been in Position 2.

We established in Explanation B that *Santa Claws* was either in Position 4 or 5. Since we know that *Christmas Tree Hugger* was in Position 5, *Santa Claws* must have been in Position 4.

Candle name	Ice lantern	Burning time	Position
Bah-Hum-Pug	Cube		2
Christmas Tree Hugger			5
Love You Snow Much			1
Santa Claws	Pyramid		4
Whisking You a Merry Christmas			3

E. Clue 5 states that the candle that poked well above the ice lantern had the longest burning time. We established in Explanation C that *Christmas Tree Hugger* did not fit inside its ice lantern. Therefore, it was *Christmas Tree Hugger* that had the longest burning time – which was 21 microcenturies.

Candle name	Ice lantern	Burning time	Position
Bah-Hum-Pug	Cube		2
Christmas Tree Hugger		21 microcenturies	5
Love You Snow Much			1
Santa Claws	Pyramid		4
Whisking You a Merry Christmas			3

F. Clue 3 states that the burning time of *Whisking You a Merry Christmas* was 1 microcentury less than the candle that was positioned immediately to the west of Santa's favorite tree. When we look at the picture, we can see that it's the candle in Position 2 that is immediately west of the tree. We know that the candle in Position 2 was *Bah-Hum-Pug*. This is to say that the burning time of *Whisking You a Merry Christmas* was 1 microcentury less than the burning time of *Bah-Hum-Pug*. Since the burning time of *Christmas Tree Hugger* was 21 microcenturies, the burning time of neither *Whisking You a Merry Christmas* nor *Bah-Hum-Pug* can be 21 microcenturies. When we look at the remaining burning time options, there are 2 possible combinations:

1. If the burning time of *Whisking You a Merry Christmas* was 19 microcenturies, the burning time of *Bah-Hum-Pug* was 20 microcenturies.
2. If the burning time of *Whisking You a Merry Christmas* was 16 microcenturies, the burning time of *Bah-Hum-Pug* was 17 microcenturies.

Candle name: Bah-Hum-Pug = Burning time: 17 microcenturies OR 20 microcenturies
Candle name: Whisking You a Merry Christmas = Burning time: 16 microcenturies OR 19 microcenturies

G. Clue 4 states that the candles whose combined burning time was 35 microcenturies weren't positioned next to each other. When we look at the burning time options, we can see that there is only 1 combination that is feasible: the burning times of these candles have to be 16 microcenturies and 19 microcenturies. We established in Explanation F that the burning time of *Whisking You a Merry Christmas* was either 16 microcenturies or 19 microcenturies. Therefore, *Whisking You a Merry Christmas* has to be one of the candles whose combined burning time was 35 microcenturies.

As mentioned above, Clue 4 states that these candles weren't positioned next to each other. We know that *Whisking You a Merry Christmas* was in Position 3. Candles that are not next to Position 3 are Positions 1 and 5. However, we know that the candle in Position 5, which was called *Christmas Tree Hugger*, had a burning time of 21 microcenturies. Therefore, it cannot be part of the pair whose combined burning time was 35 microcenturies (which we know is the combination of 16 microcenturies and 19 microcenturies). It follows from this that the candle in Position 1 has to be the candle that was part of the pair whose combined burning time was 35 microcenturies. We know that it was *Love You Snow Much* that was in Position 1. Therefore, it's *Love You Snow Much* and *Whisking You a Merry Christmas* whose combined burning time was 35 microcenturies. This is to say, of *Love You Snow Much* and *Whisking You a Merry Christmas*, one had the burning time of 16 microcenturies and the other 19 microcenturies (but not necessarily in this order).

Candles whose combined burning time was 35 microcenturies: Love You Snow Much AND Whisking You a Merry Christmas
Candle name: Love You Snow Much = Burning time: 16 microcenturies OR 19 microcenturies

Candle name: Whisking You a Merry Christmas = Burning time: 16 microcenturies OR 19 microcenturies

H. Clue 4 indicates that of the candles whose combined burning time was 35 microcenturies, the one that was closer to the Excellent Elf School was placed inside a sphere-shaped lantern. We established in Explanation G that it was *Love You Snow Much* and *Whisking You a Merry Christmas* that were the candles whose combined burning time was 35 microcenturies. We also know that *Love You Snow Much* was in Position 1 and *Whisking You a Merry Christmas* was in Position 3. Clue 1 explains that the Excellent Elf School was in the west and Santa's workshop was in the east. Therefore, it was *Love You Snow Much* that was closer to the Excellent Elf School. It follows from this that *Love You Snow Much* must have been placed inside a sphere-shaped ice lantern.

Candle name	Ice lantern	Burning time	Position
Bah-Hum-Pug	Cube		2
Christmas Tree Hugger		21 microcenturies	5
Love You Snow Much	Sphere		1
Santa Claws	Pyramid		4
Whisking You a Merry Christmas			3

I. Clue 5 indicates that the candle with the longest burning time was closer to Santa's workshop than the candle whose burning time was 3 microcenturies less than the candle called *Love You Snow Much*. This is to say that one of the candles had a burning time that was 3 microcenturies less than the burning time of *Love You Snow Much*. We established in Explanation G that *Love You Snow Much* had a burning time of either 16 microcenturies or 19 microcenturies. For another candle to have a burning time that is 3 microcenturies less means that the burning time of *Love You Snow Much* cannot be 16 microcenturies – as this is the shortest burning time – and, hence, has to be 19 microcenturies.

We established in Explanation G that *Whisking You a Merry Christmas* had a burning time of either 16 microcenturies or 19 microcenturies. Since *Love You Snow Much* had a burning time of 19 microcenturies, *Whisking You a Merry Christmas* must have had a burning time of 16 microcenturies.

Candle name	Ice lantern	Burning time	Position
Bah-Hum-Pug	Cube		2
Christmas Tree Hugger		21 microcenturies	5
Love You Snow Much	Sphere	19 microcenturies	1
Santa Claws	Pyramid		4
Whisking You a Merry Christmas		16 microcenturies	3

J. Clue 3 indicates that *Whisking You a Merry Christmas* had a burning time that was 1 microcentury less than the candle that was positioned immediately west of Santa's favorite tree. We established in Explanation F that Position 2 is immediately west of the tree and this was where *Bah-Hum-Pug* was placed. Therefore, we can rephrase Clue 3 as follows: *Whisking You a Merry Christmas* had a burning time that was 1 microcentury less than the burning time of *Bah-Hum-Pug*. We know that the burning time of *Whisking You a Merry Christmas* was 16 microcenturies. Hence, the burning time of *Bah-Hum-Pug* must have been 17 microcenturies.

Since *Bah-Hum-Pug* had a burning time of 17 microcenturies, *Christmas Tree Hugger* had a burning time of 21 microcenturies, *Love You Snow Much* had a burning time of 19 microcenturies, and *Whisking You a Merry Christmas* had a burning time of 16 microcenturies, it must be *Santa Claws* whose burning time was 20 microcenturies.

Candle name	Ice lantern	Burning time	Position
Bah-Hum-Pug	Cube	17 microcenturies	2
Christmas Tree Hugger		21 microcenturies	5
Love You Snow Much	Sphere	19 microcenturies	1
Santa Claws	Pyramid	20 microcenturies	4
Whisking You a Merry Christmas		16 microcenturies	3

K. Clue 2 indicates that there was a candle whose burning time was 2 microcenturies less than the burning time of the candle that was inside a cone-shaped lantern. We know that *Bah-Hum-Pug* was inside a cube-shaped

80

lantern, *Love You Snow Much* was inside a sphere-shaped ice lantern, and *Santa Claws* was inside a pyramid-shaped ice lantern. Therefore, it's either *Christmas Tree Hugger* or *Whisking You a Merry Christmas* that was placed inside a cone-shaped ice lantern. We know that *Christmas Tree Hugger* had a burning time of 21 microcenturies and *Whisking You a Merry Christmas* had a burning time of 16 microcenturies. Since there was a candle whose burning time was 2 microcenturies less than the burning time of the candle that was inside a cone-shaped lantern, 16 microcenturies – which is the shortest burning time – cannot be the burning time of the candle that was placed inside a cone-shaped ice lantern. Therefore, the candle inside the cone-shaped ice lantern must have been the one with the burning time of 21 microcenturies – which we know is *Christmas Tree Hugger*.

Since *Bah-Hum-Pug* was inside a cube-shaped lantern, *Christmas Tree Hugger* was inside a cone-shaped ice lantern, *Love You Snow Much* was inside a sphere-shaped ice lantern, and *Santa Claws* was inside a pyramid-shaped ice lantern, it must be *Whisking You a Merry Christmas* that was placed inside the cylinder-shaped lantern.

Candle name	Ice lantern	Burning time	Position
Bah-Hum-Pug	Cube	17 microcenturies	2
Christmas Tree Hugger	Cone	21 microcenturies	5
Love You Snow Much	Sphere	19 microcenturies	1
Santa Claws	Pyramid	20 microcenturies	4
Whisking You a Merry Christmas	Cylinder	16 microcenturies	3

19. Best in Snow

A. Clue 5 states that Icicle and Mittens were the only dogs who wore red collars. Clue 3 indicates that Perrie Winkle's dog wore a red collar and Clue 7 indicates that Chris Tingle's dog wore a red collar. Therefore, Icicle and Mittens were Perrie Winkle and Chris Tingle's dogs (but not necessarily in this order).

Clue 7 indicates that Chris Tingle's husky wore a red collar without any text written on it. Clue 5 indicates that one of the dogs who wore a red collar had the text, "I've been a furry good dog." on it and it was this husky that danced to *Here Comes Santa Paws*. Since Chris Tingle's husky didn't have any text written on its collar, it must be Perrie Winkle's husky who did, and consequently, it's Perrie Winkle who danced to *Here Comes Santa Paws* with her dog.

Husky: Icicle = Trainer elf: Chris Tingle OR Perrie Winkle
Husky: Mittens = Trainer elf: Chris Tingle OR Perrie Winkle
Trainer elf: Perrie Winkle = Song: Here Comes Santa Paws

B. Clue 1 indicates that the foxtrot routines weren't ranked 1st. Clue 2 indicates that the quickstep was ranked higher than the American-smooth dances. Since there is an indication that there were more than 1 foxtrot and more than 1 American smooth, and that there was 1 quickstep, we can deduce that there must have been 2 foxtrot dances, 2 American-smooth dances, and 1 quickstep. Since the foxtrot routines didn't come 1st, and the quickstep was ranked higher than the American-smooth dances, it must the quickstep that came 1st.

Clue 2 indicates that the quickstep was danced by a husky with a food-related name. When we look at the huskies' name options, we can see that it was either Cranberry or Fruitcake who must have danced the quickstep and come 1st. However, Clue 4 states that Fruitcake was ranked lower than the husky whose trainer was Tinker Belle. This means that Fruitcake cannot have come 1st. Therefore, it must be Cranberry who came 1st.

1 x Quickstep = Husky: Cranberry = Ranking: 1st
2 x Foxtrot dances
2 x American-smooth dances

Husky	Trainer elf	Song	Ranking
Cranberry			1st
Fruitcake			
Icicle			
Mittens			
Tiny Tim			

C. We established in Explanation B that Cranberry danced a quickstep and came 1st. Clue 2 indicates that *Deck the Halls with Bows on Collies* was a

song for an American smooth. Therefore, it cannot have been the song in Cranberry's performance. Clue 3 indicates that Perrie Winkle's best friend was ranked 1 place higher than the team who danced to *Go Tail It on the Mountain*. This means that the team who danced to *Go Tail It on the Mountain* cannot have come 1st. This is to say, *Go Tail It on the Mountain* cannot have been the song in Cranberry's performance. Clue 7 indicates that *Barking Around the Christmas Tree* was the song to a dance that came 2 places lower than Chris Tingle's dance. This is to say, *Barking Around the Christmas Tree* cannot have come 1st. This means that the team that danced to *Barking Around the Christmas Tree* cannot have been Cranberry's team. We also established in Explanation A that the song danced by Perrie Winkle, whose husky was either Icicle or Mittens, was *Here Comes Santa Paws*. Since Perrie Winkle wasn't Cranberry's trainer, *Here Comes Santa Paws* cannot have been the song that was danced by Cranberry. It follows from this that Cranberry must have danced to the song *Dachshund Through the Snow*.

American smooth = Song: Deck the Halls with Bows on Collies

Husky	Trainer elf	Song	Ranking
Cranberry		*Dachshund Through the Snow*	1st
Fruitcake			
Icicle			
Mittens			
Tiny Tim			

D. We established in Explanation A that Icicle and Mittens' trainers were Chris Tingle and Perrie Winkle (but not necessarily in this order). Therefore, Cranberry's trainer cannot have been Chris Tingle or Perrie Winkle. Clue 4 indicates that Tinker Belle did not dance to *Dachshund Through the Snow*. Since Cranberry did dance to *Dachshund Through the Snow*, Tinker Belle cannot have been Cranberry's trainer. Furthermore, Clue 2 indicates that Sugarplum Mary created an American-smooth routine. We established in Explanation B that Cranberry danced a quickstep. Therefore, Sugarplum Mary cannot have been Cranberry's trainer. It follows from this that Cranberry's trainer must have been Mary Light.

Husky	Trainer elf	Song	Ranking
Cranberry	Mary Light	*Dachshund Through the Snow*	1st
Fruitcake			
Icicle			
Mittens			
Tiny Tim			

E. Clue 8 states that Mary Light came 1 place higher than the elf who had trained Mittens. We know that Mary Light was Cranberry's trainer and they came 1st. Therefore, Mittens must have come 2nd.

Husky	Trainer elf	Song	Ranking
Cranberry	Mary Light	*Dachshund Through the Snow*	1st
Fruitcake			
Icicle			
Mittens			2nd
Tiny Tim			

F. Clue 3 indicates that Perrie Winkle did better than her best friend who came 1 place higher than the team that danced to *Go Tail It on the Mountain*. This is to say that there were at least 2 trainers who were ranked lower than Perrie Winkle. Since we know that Cranberry and its trainer Mary Light came 1st, it follows from this that Perrie Winkle must have come either 2nd or 3rd.

Clue 7 indicates that *Barking Around the Christmas Tree* came 2 places lower than Chris Tingle's dance. Since we know that Cranberry and its trainer Mary Light came 1st, it follows from this that Chris Tingle must have come either 2nd or 3rd, and *Barking Around the Christmas Tree* must have come either 4th or 5th.

We now know that of Perrie Winkle and Chris Tingle, one came 2nd and the other 3rd (but not necessarily in this order). If follows from this, and the fact that Mary Light and her husky Cranberry came 1st, that Sugarplum Mary and Tinker Belle must have come 4th and 5th (but not necessarily in this order).

Trainer elf: Chris Tingle = Ranking: 2nd OR 3rd
Trainer elf: Perrie Winkle = Ranking: 2nd OR 3rd
Trainer elf: Sugarplum Mary = Ranking: 4th OR 5th
Trainer elf: Tinker Belle = Ranking: 4th OR 5th
Song: Barking Around the Christmas Tree = Ranking: 4th OR 5th

G. We established in Explanation A that Icicle and Mittens were Perrie Winkle and Chris Tingle's dogs (but not necessarily in this order). We established in Explanation F that Chris Tingle and Perrie Winkle came 2nd and 3rd (but not necessarily in this order). Therefore, Icicle and Mittens must have come 2nd and 3rd. We already know that Mittens came 2nd. It follows from this that Icicle must have come 3rd.

Husky	Trainer elf	Song	Ranking
Cranberry	Mary Light	*Dachshund Through the Snow*	1st
Fruitcake			
Icicle			3rd
Mittens			2nd
Tiny Tim			

H. Clue 4 states that Fruitcake was ranked lower that the husky whose trainer was Tinker Belle. We established in Explanation F that Tinker Belle came either 4th or 5th. Since Fruitcake was ranked lower, Tinker Belle must have come 4th and Fruitcake must have come 5th.

Since Cranberry came 1st, Fruitcake came 5th, Icicle came 3rd, and Mittens came 2nd, it must be Tiny Tim who came 4th.

Now that we know that Tiny Tim came 4th and Tinker Belle came 4th, we can deduce that Tiny Tim's trainer elf must have been Tinker Belle.

We established in Explanation F that Sugarplum Mary came either 4th or 5th. Since Tinker Belle and her husky Tiny Tim came 4th, Sugarplum Mary must have come 5th. We know that Fruitcake came 5th. Therefore, Fruitcake must have been Sugarplum Mary's dog.

Husky	Trainer elf	Song	Ranking
Cranberry	Mary Light	*Dachshund Through the Snow*	1st
Fruitcake	Sugarplum Mary		5th
Icicle			3rd
Mittens			2nd
Tiny Tim	Tinker Belle		4th

I. Clue 1 explains that the foxtrot routines did not contain any tricks whereas Clue 2 indicates that the American smooth routines and the quickstep did contain tricks. Clue 3 indicates that Perrie Winkle's dance routine would have got a higher score if it had contained some tricks. This is to say, Perrie Winkle's dance routine did not contain any tricks. We can, therefore, deduce that it must have been a foxtrot. Clue 3 also mentions that *Go Tail It on the Mountain* did not contain any tricks. Therefore, it must have also been a foxtrot. We established in Explanation A that Perrie Winkle's song choice was *Here Comes Santa Paws*. Therefore, Perrie Winkle's song choice cannot have been *Go Tail It on the Mountain*.

Clue 6 states that a foxtrot came 4th. We established in Explanation F that Perrie Winkle came either 2nd or 3rd and we now know her routine was a foxtrot. Therefore, it must be the song *Go Tail It on the Mountain* that was danced as a foxtrot that came 4th. We know that Tiny Tim's performance was ranked 4th. Therefore, it was Tiny Tim who danced to *Go Tail It on the Mountain*.

Trainer elf: Perrie Winkle = Song: Here Comes Santa Paws = Foxtrot
Husky: Tiny Tim = Foxtrot

Husky	Trainer elf	Song	Ranking
Cranberry	Mary Light	*Dachshund Through the Snow*	1st
Fruitcake	Sugarplum Mary		5th
Icicle			3rd
Mittens			2nd
Tiny Tim	Tinker Belle	*Go Tail It on the Mountain*	4th

J. We established in Explanation F that the performance that was ranked 4th or 5th was danced to the song *Barking Around the Christmas Tree*. We now know that Tiny Tim's performance to the song *Go Tail It on the Mountain* was ranked 4th. Therefore, the performance to the song *Barking Around the Christmas Tree* must have been ranked 5th. We know that it was Fruitcake who came 5th. Hence, it was Fruitcake who danced to *Barking Around the Christmas Tree*.

Husky	Trainer elf	Song	Ranking
Cranberry	Mary Light	*Dachshund Through the Snow*	1st
Fruitcake	Sugarplum Mary	*Barking Around the Christmas Tree*	5th
Icicle			3rd
Mittens			2nd
Tiny Tim	Tinker Belle	*Go Tail It on the Mountain*	4th

K. Clue 7 states that *Barking Around the Christmas Tree* was a song to a dance that came 2 places lower than Chris Tingle's dance. We know that *Barking Around the Christmas Tree* was a song to which Fruitcake danced, and we also know that Fruitcake came 5th. Therefore, Chris Tingle must have come 3rd. We know that Icicle came 3rd. Therefore, Icicle must have been Chris Tingle's dog.

Since Cranberry's trainer was Mary Light, Fruitcake's trainer was Sugarplum Mary, Icicle's trainer was Chris Tingle, and Tiny Tim's trainer was Tinker Belle, it must be Perrie Winkle who was Mittens' trainer.

Husky	Trainer elf	Song	Ranking
Cranberry	Mary Light	*Dachshund Through the Snow*	1st
Fruitcake	Sugarplum Mary	*Barking Around the Christmas Tree*	5th
Icicle	Chris Tingle		3rd
Mittens	Perrie Winkle		2nd
Tiny Tim	Tinker Belle	*Go Tail It on the Mountain*	4th

L. We established in Explanation A that Perrie Winkle's song choice was *Here Comes Santa Paws*. We now know that her husky was Mittens. Therefore, it was Mittens and Perrie Winkle who formed a team and danced to *Here Comes Santa Paws*.

Since Cranberry danced to *Dachshund Through the Snow,* Fruitcake danced to *Barking Around the Christmas Tree*, Mittens danced to *Here Comes Santa Paws*, and Tiny Tim danced to *Go Tail It on the Mountain*, it must be Icicle who danced to *Deck the Halls with Bows on Collies*.

Husky	Trainer elf	Song	Ranking
Cranberry	Mary Light	*Dachshund Through the Snow*	1st
Fruitcake	Sugarplum Mary	*Barking Around the Christmas Tree*	5th
Icicle	Chris Tingle	*Deck the Halls with Bows on Collies*	3rd
Mittens	Perrie Winkle	*Here Comes Santa Paws*	2nd
Tiny Tim	Tinker Belle	*Go Tail It on the Mountain*	4th

20. Elvesdropping

A. The puzzle mentions 4 locations where the different memorable events took place: Clue 1 indicates that 2 elves observed Quince Pie Quarter, Clue 2 mentions Garland Glen, and Clue 5 mentions Feast Field and Snowfall Square. Hence, we can deduce that while 2 elves wrote about Quince Pie Quarter, 1 elf wrote about Garland Glen, another elf wrote about Feast Field, and yet another elf wrote about Snowfall Square.

B. Clue 9 indicates that Thinker Belle wrote a report about Garland Glen's inhabitants. Clue 2 describes a little girl in Garland Glen decorating her brother's bedroom walls. Therefore, we can deduce that Thinker Belle's most memorable event was seeing the brother's bedroom being decorated.

Elf: Thinker Belle = Location: Garland Glen

Elf	Event	No. of pages	Time
Blinker Belle			
Clinker Belle			
Stinker Belle			
Thinker Belle	Decorating brother's room		
Winker Belle			

C. Clue 9 indicates that the report about Snowfall Square where a car was painted was submitted 13 minutes before the midnight deadline – in other words, at 23:47. Clue 7 describes a little girl painting her mom's car door. This is to say that the report of the event of painting a mom's car was submitted at 23:47.

Clue 5 states that of the reports that gave details of events that took place in Feast Field and Snowfall Square, one was 21 pages long and the other was submitted at 11.37 pm – that is, 23:37. We know that the report about Snowfall Square was submitted at 23:47. Therefore, it must be the report about Feast Field that was submitted at 23:37 and the report about Snowfall Square – where a mom's car was painted – must have been 21 pages long.

Event: Painting mom's car = No. of pages: 21 = Time: 23:47 = Location: Snowfall Square
Time: 23:37 = Location: Feast Field

D. Clue 6 states that Clinker Belle's report was 3 pages shorter than the report that was submitted less than a quarter of an hour before midnight. We established in Explanation C that the report about Snowfall Square, which was 21 pages long was submitted at 23:47 – that is, the only time option that is less than a quarter of an hour before midnight. Therefore, Clinker Belle's report must have been 3 pages shorter than the Snowfall Square's 21 pages. This means Clinker Belle's report must have been 18 pages long.

Clue 9 indicates that Thinker Belle's report was 4 pages longer than the report that was submitted 13 minutes before the midnight deadline. We established in Explanation C that this refers to the Snowfall Square report that was submitted at 23:47 and was 21 pages long. It follows from this that Thinker Belle's report must have been 25 pages long.

Elf	Event	No. of pages	Time
Blinker Belle			
Clinker Belle		18	
Stinker Belle			
Thinker Belle	Decorating brother's room	25	
Winker Belle			

E. Clue 1 states that Blinker Belle and the elf whose report was 18 pages long spent the day in Quince Pie Quarter, and the latter jotted down a good deed by a kid whose attempt at delighting his mom didn't end in the desired outcome. We know that the elf whose report was 18 pages long was Clinker Belle. We established in Explanation C that it was in Snowfall Square where a little girl painted her mom's car door. Therefore, the event of a mom's car being painted cannot have happened in Quince Pie Quarter. When we look at the event options, only 1 feasible option remains where the recipient of the good deed was a mom: the event in Quince Pie Quarter must have been the one where a kid prepared a bath for their mom. Therefore, it is this event that Clinker Belle reported.

Elf	Event	No. of pages	Time
Blinker Belle			
Clinker Belle	Preparing mom's bath	18	
Stinker Belle			
Thinker Belle	Decorating brother's room	25	
Winker Belle			

F. Clue 8 states that of the longest and shortest reports, one contained a description of a haircut. When we look at the event options, we can see that one of them is cutting a sister's hair, so this is what the clue must be referring to. We know that the shortest report (18 pages) was by Clinker Belle and we also know that she wrote about a mom's bath preparations.

Therefore, it must be the longest report – the one that was 28 pages long – that contained a description of a sister's haircut.

Event: Cutting sister's hair = No. of pages: 28

G. Clue 4 states that the report about a brother cutting his sister's hair was submitted earlier than Thinker Belle's report, but later than the report that was 3 pages shorter than Stinker Belle's report. This clue indicates that there was an elf whose report was 3 pages shorter than Stinker Belle's report. When we look at the options regarding the number of pages, we can see that there are 2 possible combinations:

1. Stinker Belle's report was 28 pages long, and the elf whose report was 3 pages shorter wrote a report that was 25 pages long.
2. Stinker Belle's report was 21 pages long, and the elf whose report was 3 pages shorter wrote a report that was 18 pages long.

We know that it was Thinker Belle whose report was 25 pages long and Clinker Belle whose report was 18 pages long. Since Clue 4 indicates that Thinker Belle's report was submitted at a different time from the report that was 3 pages shorter than Stinker Belle's report, Thinker Belle cannot be the elf whose report was 3 pages shorter than Stinker Belle's report – otherwise, Thinker Belle's report would be compared to her own report and it would not be possible for these to be submitted at different times. It follows from this that the elf whose report was 3 pages shorter than Stinker Belle's report must have been Clinker Belle whose report was 18 pages long. This means that Stinker Belle's report, which was 3 pages longer, must have been 21 pages long.

We established in Explanation C that the report that was 21 pages long was submitted at 23:47 and it contained a description of a mom's car being painted. Since we know that it was Stinker Belle whose report was 21 pages long, it was her who wrote about a mom's car being painted and who submitted her report at 23:47.

Elf	Event	No. of pages	Time
Blinker Belle			
Clinker Belle	Preparing mom's bath	18	
Stinker Belle	Painting mom's car	21	23:47
Thinker Belle	Decorating brother's room	25	
Winker Belle			

H. We know that Clinker Belle wrote about a mom's bath preparations, Stinker Belle wrote about a mom's car being painted, and Thinker Belle wrote about a brother's room being decorated. Hence, the elf who witnessed a dad's laptop being washed was either Blinker Belle or Winker Belle. Clue 3 indicates that the elf who witnessed a dad's laptop being washed submitted her report earlier than Winker Belle. This means that Winker Belle cannot have been the elf who witnessed a dad's laptop being washed. It follows from this that it must have been Blinker Belle who witnessed a dad's laptop being washed.

Since Blinker Belle wrote about a dad's laptop being washed, Clinker Belle wrote about a mom's bath preparations, Stinker Belle wrote about a mom's car being painted, and Thinker Belle wrote about a brother's room being decorated, it must be Winker Belle who wrote about a sister's haircut.

Elf	Event	No. of pages	Time
Blinker Belle	Washing dad's laptop		
Clinker Belle	Preparing mom's bath	18	
Stinker Belle	Painting mom's car	21	23:47
Thinker Belle	Decorating brother's room	25	
Winker Belle	Cutting sister's hair		

I. We established in Explanation F that the report containing a description of a brother cutting his sister's hair was 28 pages long. We know that it was Winker Belle who wrote about a brother cutting his sister's hair. Therefore, Winker Belle's report was 28 pages long.

Since Clinker Belle's report was 18 pages long, Stinker Belle's report was 21 pages long, Thinker Belle's report was 25 pages long, and Winker Belle's report was 28 pages long, it must be Blinker Belle's report that was 23 pages long.

Elf	Event	No. of pages	Time
Blinker Belle	Washing dad's laptop	23	
Clinker Belle	Preparing mom's bath	18	
Stinker Belle	Painting mom's car	21	23:47
Thinker Belle	Decorating brother's room	25	
Winker Belle	Cutting sister's hair	28	

J. We established in Explanation C that the elf who wrote a report about Feast Field's inhabitants submitted her report at 23:37. Clue 1 indicates that Blinker Belle and the elf whose report was 18 pages long spent their day in Quince Pie Quarter. We know that it was Clinker Belle whose report was 18 pages long. Therefore, it was Clinker Belle and Blinker Belle who wrote about Quince Pie Quarter, and so, did not write about Feast Field. Clue 9 indicates that Thinker Belle wrote about Garland Glen's inhabitants. Therefore, Thinker Belle did not write about Feast Field's inhabitants either. Furthermore, we know that Stinker Belle submitted her report at 23:47. Since the report about Feast Field's inhabitants was submitted at 23:37, Stinker Belle cannot have been the writer of this report. It follows from this that the elf who wrote about Feast Field's inhabitants and submitted her report at 23:37 must have been Winker Belle.

Elf	Event	No. of pages	Time
Blinker Belle	Washing dad's laptop	23	
Clinker Belle	Preparing mom's bath	18	
Stinker Belle	Painting mom's car	21	23:47
Thinker Belle	Decorating brother's room	25	
Winker Belle	Cutting sister's hair	28	23:37

K. Clue 3 indicates that the elf who witnessed a dad's laptop being washed didn't submit her report 1st, but managed to do so earlier than Winker Belle. We know that the elf who witnessed a dad's laptop being washed was Blinker Belle. Therefore, it was Blinker Belle who didn't submit her report 1st, but did so earlier than Winker Belle. We know that Winker Belle submitted her report at 23:37. There are 2 times that are earlier than that: 23:28 and 23:29. Since Blinker Belle didn't submit her report 1st, she must have submitted it at 23:29.

Elf	Event	No. of pages	Time
Blinker Belle	Washing dad's laptop	23	23:29
Clinker Belle	Preparing mom's bath	18	
Stinker Belle	Painting mom's car	21	23:47
Thinker Belle	Decorating brother's room	25	
Winker Belle	Cutting sister's hair	28	23:37

L. Clue 4 indicates that the report about a brother cutting his sister's hair was submitted earlier than Thinker Belle's report. We know that the report about a brother cutting his sister's hair was submitted by Winker Belle at 23:37. Since this report was submitted earlier than Thinker Belle's report, there are 2 times when Thinker Belle could have submitted her report: at 23:39 or 23:47. Since it was Stinker Belle who submitted her report at 23:47, it must be at 23:39 when Thinker Belle submitted her report.

Since Blinker Belle submitted her report at 23:29, Stinker Belle submitted her report at 23:47, Thinker Belle submitted her report at 23:39, and Winker Belle submitted her report at 23:37, it must be Clinker Belle who submitted her report at 23:28.

Elf	Event	No. of pages	Time
Blinker Belle	Washing dad's laptop	23	23:29
Clinker Belle	Preparing mom's bath	18	23:28
Stinker Belle	Painting mom's car	21	23:47
Thinker Belle	Decorating brother's room	25	23:39
Winker Belle	Cutting sister's hair	28	23:37

21. A Deery Atmosphere

A. Clue 10 states that Gale Force laughed most at the joke involving Mrs Claus. When we look at the picture, we can see that the reindeer who told the joke involving Mrs Claus was in Place D. Therefore, Gale Forced laughed most at the joke told by the reindeer in Place D.

Elf	Technique	Reindeer	Place
Aurora Borealis			
Gale Force			D
Frost Bite			
Ridge Tent			
Yule Log			

B. Clue 1 indicates that the elf whose technique was the infinity focus setting on his camera was mesmerized by Glitter Nose's joke involving the word 'deer'. When we look at the picture and the jokes, we can see that there are 2 reindeer who used the word 'deer' in their jokes: the reindeer in Places D and E. However, Clue 10 indicates that the joke involving Mrs Claus – which, we can see in the picture, includes the word 'deer' – was told by a reindeer who stood next to Glitter Nose. We established in Explanation A that the reindeer who told the joke involving Mrs Claus was the reindeer in Place D. It follows from this that Glitter Nose cannot have been in Place D, but must have been in a place next to it: Place E.

Technique: Infinity focus = Reindeer: Glitter Nose = Place: E

C. Clue 5 states that Twinkle Pose was 1 of the reindeer who faced away from the Christmas tree. When we look at the picture, we can see that the reindeer in Places A, D, and E face away from the Christmas tree. However, we established in Explanation B that it was Glitter Nose who was in Place E. Therefore, Twinkle Pose must have been either in Place A or Place D.

Clue 6 states that the reindeer at whose joke Ridge Tent laughed the most stood closer to the Christmas tree than Silver Throat, and that the tails of these 2 reindeer faced each other. We established in Explanation B that Glitter Nose occupied the place that was the farthest from the Christmas tree – that is, Place E. Therefore, neither of the reindeer mentioned in Clue 6 could have occupied that place. It follows from this that since the reindeer whose joke Ridge Tent found the funniest was closer to the Christmas tree and since the tails of this reindeer and Silver Throat faced each other, this reindeer must have occupied either Place B or C, and Silver Throat must have occupied either Place A or D in the following way: if the reindeer whose joke Ridge Tent found the funniest was in Place B, Silver Throat was in Place A; and if the reindeer whose joke Ridge Tent found the funniest was in Place C, Silver Throat was in Place D.

We have now deduced that Twinkle Pose was either in Place A or Place D. We have also deduced that Silver Throat was either in Place A or Place D. Since we also know from Explanation B that Glitter Nose was in Place E, we can further deduce that of Glamor Coat and Sparkle Toes, one must have been in Place B and other in Place C (but not necessarily in this order).

We established above that the reindeer whose joke Ridge Tent found the funniest was either in Place B or Place C. Since we now know that Glamor Coat and Sparkle Toes were in Places B and C (but not necessarily in this order), this means that Ridge Tent must have found either Glamor Coat or Sparkle Toes the funniest.

Reindeer: Twinkle Pose = Place: A OR D
Reindeer: Silver Throat = Place: A OR D
Reindeer: Glamor Coat = Place: B OR C
Reindeer: Sparkle Toes = Place: B OR C
Elf: Ridge Tent = Reindeer: Glamor Coat OR Sparkle Toes = Place: B OR C

D. Clue 4 states that the joke involving Rudolph caused an elf to fall over her tripod. When we look at the picture, we can see that the joke involving Rudolph was told by the reindeer in Place A. Therefore, the technique of having a tripod was used by the elf who enjoyed the performance of the reindeer in Place A the most.

Clue 9 indicates that the elf who intended to use a wide-angle lens liked the reindeer who told a joke about Christmas tree decorations the most. When we look at the picture, we can see that the joke about the Christmas tree decorations was told by the reindeer in Place C. Therefore, the technique of a wide-angle lens was used by the elf who enjoyed the performance of the reindeer in Place C the most.

Technique: Tripod = Place: A
Technique: Wide-angle lens = Place: C

E. Clue 2 states that the elf who laughed most at the performance of the reindeer who was standing next to Sparkle Toes on the same side of the Christmas tree had her pockets full of spare batteries. We established in Explanation C that Sparkle Toes was either in Place B or Place C. If Sparkle Toes was in Place B, the reindeer next to it on the same side of the Christmas tree was the reindeer in Place A. However, we established in Explanation D that the elf who used a tripod laughed most at the joke of the reindeer who was in Place A. Therefore, this cannot have been the elf who had her pockets full of spare batteries. It follows from this that Sparkle Toes must have been in Place C. The reindeer next to Place C on the same side of the Christmas tree was in Place D. Therefore, the elf who laughed most at the joke of the reindeer who was in Place D had her pockets full of spare batteries. We know that the elf whose favorite reindeer was in Place D was Gale Force. Hence, it was Gale Force who had her pockets full of spare batteries.

Reindeer: Sparkle Toes = Place: C

Elf	Technique	Reindeer	Place
Aurora Borealis			
Gale Force	Spare batteries		D
Frost Bite			
Ridge Tent			
Yule Log			

F. We established in Explanation E that Sparkle Toes was in Place C, and in Explanation D that the elf who used a wide-angle lens liked most the reindeer in Place C. Therefore, this elf with a wide-angle lens liked most Sparkle Toes in Place C.

We established in Explanation C that Glamor Coat was either in Place B or C. Since we now know that Sparkle Toes was in Place C, Glamor Coat must have been in Place B.

Technique: Wide-angle lens = Reindeer: Sparkle Toes = Place: C
Reindeer: Glamor Coat = Place: B

G. Clue 7 states that the elf who had a spare memory card in her pocket found the joke told by the reindeer standing next to Twinkle Pose the funniest. We established in Explanation C that Twinkle Pose was either in Place A or D. When we look at the picture, we can see that Places C and E are next to Place D. If Twinkle Pose was in Place D, then the elf with a spare memory card would have enjoyed the joke of the reindeer who stood either in Place C or E. We established in Explanation D that the elf who enjoyed the performance of the reindeer in Place C used a wide-angle lens. We established in Explanation B that the elf who enjoyed the performance of the reindeer in Place E used infinity focus. Therefore, neither Place C nor Place E could be the position of the reindeer whose jokes the elf with a spare memory card found the funniest. It follows from this that Twinkle Pose must have been in Place A. When we look at the picture, we can see that the reindeer in Place B is next to the reindeer in Place A. Therefore, the reindeer in Place B must have been the one whose jokes the elf with a spare memory card found the funniest.

We have now established that Twinkle Pose was in Place A. We know from Explanation C that Silver Throat was either in Place A or Place D. Since Twinkle Pose was in Place A, Silver Throat must have been in Place D. We know that it was Gale Force who liked the jokes of the reindeer in Place D the most. Hence, Gale Force must have liked Silver Throat's jokes the most.

Reindeer: Twinkle Pose = Place: A
Technique: Spare memory card = Place: B

Elf	Technique	Reindeer	Place
Aurora Borealis			
Gale Force	Spare batteries	Silver Throat	D
Frost Bite			
Ridge Tent			
Yule Log			

H. Clue 8 states that Aurora Borealis and her brother Frost Bite laughed most at the jokes of the reindeer whose 1st names finished with the letter R. When we look at the name options in the grid, we can see that there

are 3 such names: Glamor Coat, Glitter Nose, and Silver Throat. Since we know that Silver Throat was the reindeer whose jokes Gale Force liked the most, we can deduce that Aurora Borealis and Frost Bite must have liked the jokes of Glamor Coat and Glitter Nose the most (but not necessarily in this order).

Since Gale Force liked Silver Throat's jokes the most, and since Aurora Borealis and Frost Bite liked the jokes of Glamor Coat and Glitter Nose the most (but not necessarily in this order), it follows from this that Ridge Tent and Yule Log must have liked the jokes of Sparkle Toes and Twinkle Pose the most (but not necessarily in this order).

Elf: Aurora Borealis = Reindeer: Glamor Coat OR Glitter Nose
Elf: Frost Bite = Reindeer: Glamor Coat OR Glitter Nose
Elf: Ridge Tent = Reindeer: Sparkle Toes OR Twinkle Pose
Elf: Yule Log = Reindeer: Sparkle Toes OR Twinkle Pose

I. Clue 3 states that the 2 reindeer who stood next to the Christmas tree didn't impress Yule Log that much. When we look at the picture, we can see that this clue refers to the reindeer in Places B and C. We established in Explanation H that Yule Log liked the jokes of either Sparkle Toes or Twinkle Pose the most. We established in Explanation G that Twinkle Pose was in Place A and in Explanation F that Sparkle Toes was in Place C. Since Yule Log wasn't impressed by the reindeer in Places B or C, it follows that she can't have been impressed by Sparkle Toes in Place C, and consequently, must have liked the jokes of Twinkle Pose in Place A the most.

We established in Explanation D that the elf whose technique involved a tripod liked the jokes of the reindeer in Place A the most. We now know that it was Yule Log who liked the jokes of the reindeer in Place A the most. Therefore, it must have been Yule Log who used a tripod.

Elf	Technique	Reindeer	Place
Aurora Borealis			
Gale Force	Spare batteries	Silver Throat	D
Frost Bite			
Ridge Tent			
Yule Log	Tripod	Twinkle Pose	A

J. We established in Explanation H that Ridge Tent's favorite joke was told by either Sparkle Toes or Twinkle Pose. We know that Yule Log's favorite joke was told by Twinkle Pose. Therefore, Ridge Tent's favorite joke must have been told by Sparkle Toes.

We established in Explanation F that Sparkle Toes was in Place C and the elf who found Sparkle Toes' jokes the funniest used a wide-angle lens. Since we now know that Ridge Tent found Sparkle Toes the funniest, it follows that Ridge Tent must have used a wide-angle lens and Sparkle Toes must have been in Place C.

Elf	Technique	Reindeer	Place
Aurora Borealis			
Gale Force	Spare batteries	Silver Throat	D
Frost Bite			
Ridge Tent	Wide-angle lens	Sparkle Toes	C
Yule Log	Tripod	Twinkle Pose	A

K. We know that Gale Force had spare batteries, Ridge Tent used a wide-angle lens, and Yule Log used a tripod. It follows from this that of Aurora Borealis and Frost Bite, one used infinity focus and the other had a spare memory card (but not necessarily in this order). Clue 7 indicates that the spare memory card was in the pocket of a female elf. Clue 8 indicates that Aurora Borealis was female and Frost Bite was male (Aurora's brother). Therefore, it must have been Aurora Borealis who had a spare memory card, and consequently, Frost Bite must have used infinity focus.

Elf	Technique	Reindeer	Place
Aurora Borealis	Spare memory card		
Gale Force	Spare batteries	Silver Throat	D
Frost Bite	Infinity focus		
Ridge Tent	Wide-angle lens	Sparkle Toes	C
Yule Log	Tripod	Twinkle Pose	A

L. We established in Explanation G that the elf who had a spare memory card liked the reindeer in Place B the most. We know that it was Aurora

Borealis who had a spare memory card. Therefore, she must have liked the reindeer in Place B the most. We established in Explanation F that Glamor Coat was in Place B. Therefore, Aurora Borealis must have liked Glamor Coat's performance the most.

Elf	Technique	Reindeer	Place
Aurora Borealis	Spare memory card	Glamor Coat	B
Gale Force	Spare batteries	Silver Throat	D
Frost Bite	Infinity focus		
Ridge Tent	Wide-angle lens	Sparkle Toes	C
Yule Log	Tripod	Twinkle Pose	A

M. Since Aurora Borealis found Glamor Coat in Place B the funniest, Gale Force found Silver Throat in Place D the funniest, Ridge Tent found Sparkle Toes in Place C the funniest, and Yule Log found Twinkle Pose in Place A the funniest, it must have been Frost Bite who found Glitter Nose in Place E the funniest.

Elf	Technique	Reindeer	Place
Aurora Borealis	Spare memory card	Glamor Coat	B
Gale Force	Spare batteries	Silver Throat	D
Frost Bite	Infinity focus	Glitter Nose	E
Ridge Tent	Wide-angle lens	Sparkle Toes	C
Yule Log	Tripod	Twinkle Pose	A

22. The Knotty List

A. Clue 13 states that of the elves who spent the longest doing Steps 2 and 3, one practiced tying the quick release knot and the other one was called Round Robyn. When we look at the drawing, we can see that Step 2 refers to "Practice & repetition" and Step 3 refers to "Make a song and dance about the knot".

Clue 4 indicates that Leigh Way spent the longest making a song and dance about her knot. In other words, she spent the longest doing Step 3. As stated above, Clue 13 indicates that of the elves who spent the longest doing Steps 2 and 3, one practiced tying the quick release knot and the other one was called Round Robyn. Since we know that the elf who spent the longest on Step 3 was called Leigh Way, this elf must be the one who practiced tying the quick release knot.

Elf	Knot	Time in class	Excuse
Carole Singer			
Leigh Way	Quick release knot		
Mary Tale			
Pixie Crop			
Round Robyn			

B. Clue 6 states that the student who spent longest on the practice-and-repetition step was also the one who spent the most time in Professor Knot-a-Lot's remedial class and whose excuse for not passing her exam was that she had been petting reindeer. We established in Explanation A that Step 2 was "Practice & repetition". Clue 13 states that of the elves who spent the longest doing Steps 2 and 3, one practiced tying the quick release knot and the other one was called Round Robyn. Since we know from Explanation A that the elf called Leigh Way, who spent the longest doing Step 3, was the one who practiced doing a quick release knot, the elf who spent the longest on Step 2 must have been Round Robyn. It follows from this that Round Robyn must have spent the longest in Professor Knot-a-Lot's remedial class and Round Robyn's excuse must have been that she had been petting reindeer.

To figure out Round Robyn's time in Professor Knot-a-Lot's remedial class, we need to look at the time-in-class options. There is 1 time slot that is 2 h: 16:15 – 18:15. There are 3 time slots that are 2 h 15 mins: 16.00 – 18:15, 16:15 – 18:30, and 16:30 – 18:45. There is 1 time slot that is 2 h 45 mins: 16:00 – 18:45. This is to say that the time slot 16:00 – 18:45, which is 2 h 45 mins long, is the longest. Since Round Robyn spent the longest in Professor Knot-a-Lot's remedial class, Round Robyn's time slot must have been 16:00 – 18:45.

Time in class: 16.00 – 18:15: 2 h 15 mins
Time in class: 16:15 – 18:15: 2 h
Time in class: 16:15 – 18:30: 2 h 15 mins
Time in class: 16:30 – 18:45: 2h 15 mins
Time in class: 16:00 – 18:45: 2 h 45 mins

Elf	Knot	Time in class	Excuse
Carole Singer			
Leigh Way	Quick release knot		
Mary Tale			
Pixie Crop			
Round Robyn		16:00 – 18:45	Petting reindeer

C. Clue 1 explains that the Year 1 students arrived at 4 pm – that is, 16:00 – the Year 2 students arrived 15 minutes later – that is, 16:15 – and the Year 3 student started at 4.30 pm – that is, 16:30. When we look at the time-in-class options, we can see that 16:00 – 18:15 and 16:00 – 16:45 were the slots for the Year 1 students, 16:15 – 18:15 and 16:15 – 18:30 were the slots for the Year 2 students, and 16:30 – 18:45 was the slot for the Year 3 student.

Clue 14 states that Carole Singer finished the remedial class earlier than the elf who used the song *Neigh Bells Sing* in her performance. Clue 5 indicates that the student who used the song *Neigh Bells Sing* in her performance was a 2nd year student. Clue 3 indicates that Carole Singer had mastered the bow tie the previous year and that the bow tie was included in the Year 1 curriculum. It follows from this that Carole Singer must have been a 2nd year student. So, Carole Singer and the elf who used the song *Neigh Bells Sing* in her performance were both Year 2 students. We established above that the Year 2 time slots were 16:15 – 18:15 and 16:15 – 18:30. For Carole Singer to finish the remedial class earlier than the elf who used the song *Neigh Bells Sing* in her performance, she must have had the time slot 16:15 – 18:15 and the elf who used the song *Neigh Bells Sing* in her performance must have had the time slot 16:15 – 18:30.

Year 1 = 16:00 – 18:15 and 16:00 – 16:45 (2 students)
Year 2 = 16:15 – 18:15 and 16:15 – 18:30 (2 students)
Year 3 = 16:30 – 18:45 (1 student)

The elf who used the song Neigh Bells Ring in her performance = Time in class: 16:15 – 18:30 (Year 2 student)

Elf	Knot	Time in class	Excuse
Carole Singer		16:15 – 18:15	
Leigh Way	Quick release knot		
Mary Tale			
Pixie Crop			
Round Robyn		16:00 – 18:45	Petting reindeer

D. Clue 7 indicates that of the elves who spent the same amount of time in the remedial class, one of them (who started the class 15 mins earlier than Pixie Crop) rapped to the tune of *Who Let the Elves Out*. We established in Explanation B that there were 3 time slots that were 2 h 15 mins, 1 slot that was 2 h, and 1 slot that was 2 h 45 mins. As Clue 7 refers to elves who spent the same amount of time in the remedial class, this must mean the 3 elves who spent 2 h 15 mins in the remedial class: in other words, the slots 16.00 – 18:15, 16:15 – 18:30, and 16:30 – 18:45.

We established in Explanation C that the elf who used the song *Neigh Bells Ring* in her performance had the time slot 16:15 – 18:30. Therefore, this cannot be the time slot of the elf who rapped to the tune of *Who Let the Elves Out*. Furthermore, Clue 7 indicates that the elf who rapped to the tune of *Who Let the Elves Out* started the class 15 mins earlier than Pixie Crop. This means that the elf who rapped to the tune of *Who Let the Elves Out* cannot have had the latest start time – in other words, the slot 16:30 – 18:45. It follows from this that the elf who rapped to the tune of *Who Let the Elves Out* must have had the slot 16.00 – 18:15.

Clue 7 indicates that the elf who rapped to the tune of *Who Let the Elves Out* started the class 15 mins earlier than Pixie Crop. We now know that this elf's slot was 16.00 – 18:15. It follows from this that Pixie Crop's start time must have been 16:15. There are 2 slots that start at this time: 16:15 – 18:15 and 16:15 – 18:30. Since we know that Carole Singer's slot was 16:15 – 18:15, the slot 16:15 – 18:30 must have been when Pixie Crop was in the remedial class.

The elf who rapped to the song Who Let the Elves Out = Time in class: 16:00 – 18:15 (Year 1 student)

Elf	Knot	Time in class	Excuse
Carole Singer		16:15 – 18:15	
Leigh Way	Quick release knot		
Mary Tale			
Pixie Crop		16:15 – 18:30	
Round Robyn		16:00 – 18:45	Petting reindeer

E. Clue 12 states that the elf who fell asleep was the one who got through Professor Knot-a-Lot's 4-step process the fastest. We established in Explanation B that the fastest time was 2 h and this time slot was 16:15 – 18:15. We know that this time slot was Carole Singer's time slot. Therefore, it was Carole Singer who fell asleep.

Elf	Knot	Time in class	Excuse
Carole Singer		16:15 – 18:15	Fell asleep
Leigh Way	Quick release knot		
Mary Tale			
Pixie Crop		16:15 – 18:30	
Round Robyn		16:00 – 18:45	Petting reindeer

F. We know that Carole Singer's time in class was 16:15 – 18:15, Pixie Crop's time in class was 16:15 – 18:30, and Round Robyn's time in class was 16:00 – 18:45. It follows from this that of Leigh Way and Mary Tale, one's time slot was 16:00 – 18:15 and the other's time slot was 16:30 – 18:45 (but not necessarily in this order).

Clue 4 indicates that if Leigh Way hadn't found it so difficult to make a song and dance about her knot, she would have finished earlier than the elf who had been playing ice hockey instead of revising for their exam. This means that Leigh Way's end time was not the earliest. When we look at the time-in-class options, we can see that the earliest possible end time was 18:15. It follows form this that Leigh Way's time slot cannot have been 16:00 – 18:15, and it must have been 16:30 – 18:45. Consequently, Mary Tale's time slot must have been 16:00 – 18:15

Elf	Knot	Time in class	Excuse
Carole Singer		16:15 – 18:15	Fell asleep
Leigh Way	Quick release knot	16:30 – 18:45	
Mary Tale		16:00 – 18:15	
Pixie Crop		16:15 – 18:30	
Round Robyn		16:00 – 18:45	Petting reindeer

G. Clue 9 indicates that the elf who got tangled in fairy lights was in a lower year group than when the icicle hitch and the quick release knot were taught. We know that the quick release knot was the knot that Leigh Way had to learn and that her time in class started at 16:30. We established in Explanation C that the start time of 16:30 was the start time of a Year 3 student. We don't know which year the icicle hitch would have been taught, but since the elf who got tangled in fairy lights was in a lower year group, it follows that the icicle hitch must have been a Year 2 knot and the elf who got tangled in fairy lights must have been a Year 1 student.

We know from Explanation C that Year 2 students' times in class were 16:15 – 18:15 and 16:15 – 18:30. Therefore, the icicle hitch was learned during either of these times. We know that Carole Singer was in class 16:15 – 18:15 and Pixie Crop was in class 16:15 – 18:30. Hence, it was either Carole Singer or Pixie Crop who learned the icicle hitch.

We know from Explanation C that Year 1 students' times in class were 16:00 – 18:15 and 16:00 – 16:45. Therefore, the elf who got tangled in fairy lights must have been in the remedial class during either of these time slots. However, we know that the elf whose excuse was petting reindeer was in class 16:00 – 18:45. Therefore, the elf who got tangled in fairy lights must have been in class 16:00 – 18:15. We know that it was Mary Tale who was in the remedial class during this time. Hence, it must be Mary Tale who got tangled in fairy lights.

Elf: Carole Singer OR Pixie Crop = Knot: Icicle hitch

Elf	Knot	Time in class	Excuse
Carole Singer		16:15 – 18:15	Fell asleep
Leigh Way	Quick release knot	16:30 – 18:45	
Mary Tale		16:00 – 18:15	Tangled in fairy lights
Pixie Crop		16:15 – 18:30	
Round Robyn		16:00 – 18:45	Petting reindeer

H. We know that Carole Singer's excuse was falling asleep, Mary Tale's excuse was being tangled in fairy lights, and Round Robyn's excuse was petting reindeer. It follows from this that of Leigh Way and Pixie Crop, one's excuse was playing ice hockey and the other's excuse was getting trapped in the pantry.

Clue 4 indicates that Leigh Way would have finished earlier than the elf who was playing ice hockey instead of revising for their exam if she hadn't found it so difficult to make a song and dance about her knot. Since Leigh Way is compared with the elf who was playing ice hockey, this means that Leigh Way cannot have been the elf whose excuse was playing ice hockey. It follows from this that Leigh Way's excuse must have been getting trapped in the pantry. Consequently, we can deduce that it must have been Pixie Crop whose excuse was playing ice hockey.

Elf	Knot	Time in class	Excuse
Carole Singer		16:15 – 18:15	Fell asleep
Leigh Way	Quick release knot	16:30 – 18:45	Trapped in pantry
Mary Tale		16:00 – 18:15	Tangled in fairy lights
Pixie Crop		16:15 – 18:30	Playing ice hockey
Round Robyn		16:00 – 18:45	Petting reindeer

I. Clue 8 indicates that the elf who got trapped in the pantry finished the remedial class 15 minutes after the elf who had been learning the manger hitch. We know that it was Leigh Way who got trapped in the pantry and she finished her remedial class at 18:45. Therefore, the elf who learned the manger hitch must have finished the remedial class at 18:30. When we look at the time-in-class options, there is only 1 elf who finished the remedial class at 18:30: This was Pixie Crop whose slot was 16:15 – 18:30. Therefore, it was Pixie Crop who learned the manger hitch.

We established in Explanation G that it was either Carole Singer or Pixie Crop who learned the icicle hitch. Now that we know that Pixie Crop learned the manger hitch, we can deduce that it must have been Carole Singer who learned the icicle hitch.

Elf	Knot	Time in class	Excuse
Carole Singer	Icicle hitch	16:15 – 18:15	Fell asleep
Leigh Way	Quick release knot	16:30 – 18:45	Trapped in pantry
Mary Tale		16:00 – 18:15	Tangled in fairy lights
Pixie Crop	Manger hitch	16:15 – 18:30	Playing ice hockey
Round Robyn		16:00 – 18:45	Petting reindeer

J. Clue 11 states that the elves who incorporated *Neigh Bells Ring* and *Who Let the Elves Out* into their performances learned the package tying knot and the manger hitch (but not necessarily in this order).

We established in Explanation C that the elf who used the song *Neigh Bells Ring* in her performance had the time slot 16:15 – 18:30. We know that this was Pixie Crop. We established in Explanation D that the elf who used the song *Who Let the Elves Out* in her performance had the time slot 16:00 – 18:15. We know that this was Mary Tale. We also know that Pixie Crop learned the manger hitch. Therefore, it must be Mary Tale who learned the package tying knot.

Since we know that Carole Singer learned the icicle hitch, Leigh Way learned the quick release knot, Mary Tale learned the package tying knot, and Pixie Crop learned the manger hitch, it must be Round Robyn who learned the bow tie.

Elf	Knot	Time in class	Excuse
Carole Singer	Icicle hitch	16:15 – 18:15	Fell asleep
Leigh Way	Quick release knot	16:30 – 18:45	Trapped in pantry
Mary Tale	Package tying knot	16:00 – 18:15	Tangled in fairy lights
Pixie Crop	Manger hitch	16:15 – 18:30	Playing ice hockey
Round Robyn	Bow tie	16:00 – 18:45	Petting reindeer

23. Gangsta Wrappers

A. Clue 5 indicates that Elf Costello had a younger brother and an older brother. Clue 10 indicates that Elf Capone had 2 older brothers. This means that Elf Capone must have been Elf Costello's younger brother. Clue 11 indicates that Elf Pacino had younger brothers. This means that Elf Pacino must have been the eldest brother.

Youngest brother: Elf Capone
Middle brother: Elf Costello
Eldest brother: Elf Pacino

B. Clue 6 indicates that A December to Remember was a stripy wrapping paper. Clue 7 indicates that Pine-ing for You depicted a fir tree forest. Clue 8 indicates that Who Deers Wins portrayed a herd of deer, and Glad Slidings showed little elflings sliding around on a frozen lake. There is no direct description of what the Mare-y Christmas wrapping depicted, but Clue 3 indicates that there was 1 wrapping paper pattern that had frolicking horses on it. Since we know what all the other wrapping paper designs were, we can deduce that Mare-y Christmas must have depicted the frolicking horses.

Clue 5 states that of the 2 wrapping paper patterns that portrayed animals, one was created by Elf Costello's younger brother and the other was created by Elf Costello's older brother. We established in Explanation A that Elf Costello's younger brother was Elf Capone and his older brother was Elf Pacino. Hence, we can express Clue 5 as follows: Of the 2 wrapping paper patterns that portrayed animals, one was created by Elf Capone and the other was created by Elf Pacino.

We established above that Mare-y Christmas depicted frolicking horses and Who Deers Wins depicted a herd of deer. These were the only animal-themed wrapping paper designs. Hence, it is Mare-y Christmas and Who Deers Wins which were created by Elf Capone and Elf Pacino (but not necessarily in this order).

Clue 3 states that Elf Pacino spent less time on his entry than the elf whose wrapping paper depicted frolicking horses. Since Elf Pacino is compared to the elf whose wrapping paper depicted frolicking horses, he cannot be the elf who designed it. It follows from this that it must be Elf Capone who created the wrapping paper depicting frolicking horses – which we know was called Mare-y Christmas. Consequently, this means that Elf Pacino must have created Who Deers Wins.

Elf	Present	Theme	Time
Elf Capone		Mare-y Christmas	
Elf Costello			
Elfie Solomons			
Elf Pacino		Who Deers Wins	
Elfy Kimber			

C. Clue 1 indicates that the 2 cousins who collaborated in writing the lyrics for their hit song *Rebel without a Claus* were the fastest to finish their tasks. When we look at the time options, we can see that the fastest times are 1 h 47 mins and 1 h 52 mins. Clue 5 indicates that the eldest brother was a collaborator in the song *Rebel without a Claus*. We established in Explanation A that the eldest brother was Elf Pacino. This means that Elf Pacino's wrapping time was either 1 h 47 mins or 1 h 52 mins.

Since it was the 2 cousins who wrote the lyrics to *Rebel without a Claus*, we can deduce that the other cousin cannot have been Elf Pacino's brothers Elf Capone or Elf Costello. It follows from this that Elf Capone and Elf Costello's wrapping times must have been 2 of the following: 2 h 7 mins, 2 h 11 mins, or 2 h 18 mins (but not necessarily in this order). We can also deduce that the cousin (i.e. the other songwriter) must have been either Elfie Solomons or Elfy Kimber, and one of them had the wrapping time of 1 h 47 mins or 1 h 52 mins and the other had a wrapping time of 2 h 7 mins, 2 h 11 mins, or 2 h 18 mins.

Elf: Elf Pacino = Time: 1 h 47 mins OR 1 h 52 mins
Elf: Elf Capone = Time: 2 h 7 mins OR 2 h 11 mins OR 2 h 18 mins
Elf: Elf Costello = Time: 2 h 7 mins OR 2 h 11 mins OR 2 h 18 mins
Of Elfie Solomons and Elfy Kimber, one had the time 1 h 47 mins OR 1 h 52 mins and the other had the time 2 h 7 mins OR 2 h 11 mins OR 2 h 18 mins

D. Clue 4 states that the wrapping paper with the red ribbon was the creation of the elf who took longer to create his present than Elf Capone, but not as long as the elf who wrapped a handbag inside Present B. This means

that there were at least 2 presents that took longer to create than Elf Capone's present. We established in Explanation C that Elf Capone's time was 2 h 7 mins, 2 h 11 mins, or 2 h 18 mins. Since there were at least 2 presents that took longer to wrap, Elf Capone's time must have been 2 h 7 mins.

Since the wrapping paper with the red ribbon took longer to create than Elf Capone's time of 2 h 7 mins, but not as long as Present B that contained a handbag, we can deduce that the wrapping paper with a red ribbon must have taken 2 h 11 mins to create and Present B that contained a handbag must have taken 2 h 18 mins.

Present with a red ribbon = Time: 2 h 11 mins
Present: B = Time: 2 h 18 mins = This present contained a handbag

Elf	Present	Theme	Time
Elf Capone		Mare-y Christmas	2 h 7 mins
Elf Costello			
Elfie Solomons			
Elf Pacino		Who Deers Wins	
Elfy Kimber			

E. Clue 9 states that the present that touched all the other presents took 7 mins less time to submit than the present of a handbag. We established in Explanation D that a handbag was inside Present B and its wrapping time was 2 h 18 mins. We can see from the picture that Present C is the present that touches all the other presents. Hence, for Present C's wrapping time to be 7 minutes less than Present D's wrapping time of 2 h 18 mins, Present C's wrapping time must have been 2 h 11 mins.

We established in Explanation D that the wrapping time of the present with a red ribbon was 2 h 11 mins. We now know that it was Present C whose wrapping time was 2 h 11 mins. Therefore, it was Present C that had the red ribbon.

Present: C = Time: 2 h 11 mins = Had a red ribbon

F. Clue 5 indicates that Elf Costello's younger brother's present was farther away from Elfred Hitchcock's left hand than Elf Costello's elder brother's present. Let's figure out where Elf Costello's younger brother's present could be.

We know from Explanation A that Elf Costello's younger brother was Elf Capone. We also know that Elf Capone's wrapping time was 2 h 7 mins. We established in Explanations D and E that Present B's wrapping time was 2 h 18 mins and Present C's wrapping time was 2 h 11 mins. Therefore, Presents B and C cannot have been Elf Capone's presents. Clue 6 indicates that the wrapping paper called A December to Remember that had a dark green ribbon was wrapped around Present D. Since Elf Capone's wrapping paper was Mare-y Christmas, Present D cannot have been his present. It follows from this that Elf Capone's present must have been either A or E.

When we look at the picture, we can see that Present A is on the left and Present E is on the right. Clue 5 indicates that Elf Pacino's present was farther away from Elfred Hitchcock's left hand. As we are looking at Elfred Hitchcock in the same way as we would look at a photograph, his left hand is to the right side of the picture and his right hand is to the left side of the picture. Therefore, Present A is near his right hand and Present E is near his left hand. Since Elf Pacino's present was farther away from Elfred Hitchcock's left hand, it must have been closer to his right hand – which means, it must have been Present A.

Present: D = Theme: A December to Remember = Had a green ribbon

Elf	Present	Theme	Time
Elf Capone	A	Mare-y Christmas	2 h 7 mins
Elf Costello			
Elfie Solomons			
Elf Pacino		Who Deers Wins	
Elfy Kimber			

G. Clue 8 indicates that the wrapping papers Who Deers Wins and Glad Slidings were not accompanied by a red ribbon. We established in Explanation E that Present C had a red ribbon. Therefore, Present C's wrapping paper cannot have been Who Deers Wins or Glad Slidings. We also know that Present A's wrapping paper was Mare-y Christmas and we established in Explanation F that Present D's wrapping paper was A December to Remember. Hence, Present C's wrapping paper cannot have been Mare-y Christmas or A December to Remember either. It follows from this that Present C's wrapping paper must have been Pine-ing for You.

Present: C = Theme: Pine-ing for You

H. Clue 7 states that Elfy Kimber spent longer creating his competition entry than the elf who created the Pine-ing for You wrapping paper. We know from Explanation G that it was Present C that was wrapped inside the Pine-ing for You wrapping paper, and we know from Explanation E that Present C's creation time was 2 h 11 mins. Since Elfy Kimber's time was longer than Present C's time of 2 h 11 mins, his time must have been 2 h 18 mins.

We established in Explanation D that Present B took 2 h 18 minutes to create. Now that we know that Elfy Kimber's present took 2 h 18 mins to create, we can deduce that Present B must have been his.

Elf	Present	Theme	Time
Elf Capone	A	Mare-y Christmas	2 h 7 mins
Elf Costello			
Elfie Solomons			
Elf Pacino		Who Deers Wins	
Elfy Kimber	B		2 h 18 mins

I. We established in Explanation C that Elf Costello's time was 2 h 7 mins, 2 h 11 mins, or 2 h 18 mins. We now know that Elf Capone's time was 2 h 7 mins and Elfy Kimber's time was 2 h 18 mins. Therefore, Elf Costello's time must have been 2 h 11 minutes.

We established in Explanation E that Present C's wrapping time was 2 h 11 mins and in Explanation G that Present C's theme was Pine-ing for You. Since Elf Costello's time was 2 h 11 mins, it follows that his present must have been the Pine-ing for You themed Present C.

Elf	Present	Theme	Time
Elf Capone	A	Mare-y Christmas	2 h 7 mins
Elf Costello	C	Pine-ing for You	2 h 11 mins
Elfie Solomons			
Elf Pacino		Who Deers Wins	
Elfy Kimber	B		2 h 18 mins

J. Clue 11 states that of the Santa action doll present and the present whose wrapping paper incorporated the green satin ribbon, one was created the fastest and the other by one of Elf Pacino's younger brothers. We established in Explanation A that Elf Pacino's younger brothers were Elf Capone and Elf Costello. We established in Explanation F that it was Present D with a theme A December to Remember that had a green ribbon. We know that Elf Capone and Elf Costello's presents were A and C. Therefore, they cannot have wrapped Present D that had the green ribbon. Hence, one of them must have wrapped the present that contained a Santa action doll. It follows from this that Present D must have been created fastest – that is, in 1 h 47 mins.

We know that Elf Capone's present was A, Elf Costello's present was C, and Elfy Kimber's present was B. Therefore, Present D must have been either Elfie Solomons or Elf Pacino's. However, since Present D's theme was A December to Remember, and Elf Pacino's theme was Who Deers Wins, Elf Pacino cannot have been the creator of Present D. It follows from this that Elfie Solomons must have been the creator of Present D whose theme was A December to Remember and whose creation time was 1 h 47 mins.

Elf: Elf Capone OR Elf Costello = Santa action doll

Elf	Present	Theme	Time
Elf Capone	A	Mare-y Christmas	2 h 7 mins
Elf Costello	C	Pine-ing for You	2 h 11 mins
Elfie Solomons	D	A December to Remember	1 h 47 mins
Elf Pacino		Who Deers Wins	
Elfy Kimber	B		2 h 18 mins

K. We know that Elf Capone's present was A, Elf Costello's present was C, Elfie Solomons' present was D, and Elfy Kimber's present was B. Therefore, Present E must have been Elf Pacino's.

We know that Elf Capone's theme was Mare-y Christmas, Elf Costello's theme was Pine-ing for You, Elfie Solomons' theme was A December to Remember, and Elf Pacino's theme was Who Deers Wins. Therefore, it must be Elfy Kimber whose theme was Glad Slidings.

We know that Elf Capone's time was 2 h 7 mins, Elf Costello's time was 2 h 11 mins, Elfie Solomons' time was 1 h 47 mins, and Elfy Kimber's time was 2 h 18 mins. Therefore, Elf Pacino's time must have been 1 h 52 mins.

Elf	Present	Theme	Time
Elf Capone	A	Mare-y Christmas	2 h 7 mins
Elf Costello	C	Pine-ing for You	2 h 11 mins
Elfie Solomons	D	A December to Remember	1 h 47 mins
Elf Pacino	E	Who Deers Wins	1 h 52 mins
Elfy Kimber	B	Glad Slidings	2 h 18 mins

24. Easier Sleigh'd Than Done

A. Clue 1 states that the elf whose task it was to stack the presents into the sleigh was the only one who placed them where they should be: behind the bench. When we look at the diagram, we can see that Place 1 is the area behind the bench. Therefore, we can deduce that the presents' intended place was 1 and their actual place was 1.

Essential items: Presents = Intended place: 1 = Actual place: 1

B. Clue 6 indicates that the elf whose job it was to pack the presents started working before the other elves and remained packing the sleigh after everyone else had finished their task. We know from Explanation A that the presents were the only items that ended up where they were supposed to: in Place 1.

Clue 3 indicates that Henny Questions discovered that the place that had been reserved for her was already in use when she arrived. This is to say, she can't have been the elf who started working before the other elves and continued working after the other elves had finished. In other words, she cannot have been the elf who packed the presents in Place 1.

Clue 7 indicates that Joanna Hand and Anya Tows finished packing earlier than Henny Questions. This means that neither Joanna Hand nor Anya Tows was the elf who started working before the other elves and continued working after the other elves had finished. In other words, neither of them was the elf who packed the presents in Place 1.

Clue 2 indicates that Hansen Pockets was supposed to have packed his item on the right-hand side of the sleigh. When we look at the diagram, we can see that the right-hand side areas are Places 2 and 4. This means that he cannot have packed the presents in Place 1.

It follows from this that it must have been Betty B. Ready who packed the presents. We established in Explanation A that the presents' intended place was 1 and their actual place was also 1.

Elf: Hansen Pockets = Intended place: 2 OR 4 (right-hand side)

Elf	Essential items	Intended place	Actual place
Anya Tows			
Hansen Pockets			
Henny Questions			
Betty B. Ready	Presents	1	1
Joanna Hand			

C. Clue 6 states that Anya Tows' allocated compartment was on the right-hand side of the sleigh, but her item ended up on the left-hand side. When we look at the diagram, we can see that Places 2 and 4 are on the right-hand side and Places 3 and 5 are on the left-hand side. Hence, Anya Tows' intended place must have been either Place 2 or 4, and her actual place must have been either Place 3 or 5.

Elf: Anya Tows = Intended place: 2 OR 4 (right-hand side) = Actual place: 3 OR 5 (left-hand side)

D. We established in Explanations B and C that the intended places of Hansen Pockets and Anya Tows were the right-hand side places: that is, Places 2 and 4 (but not necessarily in this order). Clue 2 states that of the items that were supposed to have been packed on the right-hand side, one was packed by Hansen Pockets and the other item was the Very Important Maps satchel. It follows that the Very Important Maps satchel must have been packed by Anya Tows.

Elf	Essential items	Intended place	Actual place
Anya Tows	Very Important Maps satchel		
Hansen Pockets			
Henny Questions			
Betty B. Ready	Presents	1	1
Joanna Hand			

E. We established in Explanations B and C that the intended places of Hansen Pockets and Anya Tows were the right-hand side areas: that is, Places 2 and 4 (but not necessarily in this order). Since Betty B. Ready's intended place was 1, it follows that the intended places of Henny Questions and Joanna Hand must have been 3 and 5 (but not necessarily in this order) – these were the left-hand side areas.

Elf: Henny Questions = Intended place: 3 OR 5 (left-hand side)
Elf: Joanna Hand = Intended place: 3 OR 5 (left-hand side)

F. Clue 3 indicates that Henny Questions discovered that the place reserved for her was already occupied and, hence, she decided to use another compartment. The clue continues to explain that this compartment's number was higher than the compartment number that had originally been allocated. We established in Explanation E that Henny Questions' intended area was either Place 3 or 5. Since the actual place number where she ended up putting her item was higher than the number of her intended area, we can deduce that her intended place must have been 3, and the actual place must have been either 4 or 5.

We established in Explanation E that Joanna Hand's intended place was either 3 or 5. We now know that Henny Questions' intended place was 3. Therefore, Joanna Hand's intended place must have been 5.

Elf: Henny Questions = Actual place: 4 OR 5

Elf	Essential items	Intended place	Actual place
Anya Tows	Very Important Maps satchel		
Hansen Pockets			
Henny Questions		3	
Betty B. Ready	Presents	1	1
Joanna Hand		5	

G. Clue 3 indicates that Henny Questions discovered that the place reserved for her was already in use when she got to the sleigh. We know that Betty B. Ready placed the presents in their intended place and, therefore, didn't use the place reserved for Henny Questions. Clue 7 states that Joanna Hand and Anya Tows finished packing earlier than Henny Questions. This means that Joanna Hand and Anya Tows could have potentially taken the place intended for Henny Questions' item, as could Hansen Pockets. However, Clue 9 indicates that Joanna Hand put her item in the place that was supposed to have been Hansen Pocket's place. Therefore, Joanna Hand cannot have put her item where Henny Questions' item should have been. Also, Clue 9 indicates Hansen Pockets was the last person to pack his item in the sleigh. Hence, he must have packed his item later than Henny Questions. This means that he cannot have packed his item in the place that was intended for Henny Questions' item. It follows from this that the place intended for Henny Questions' item was taken by Anya Tows. We know that Henny Questions' intended place was 3. Therefore, we can deduce that the actual place for Anya Tows' item must have been Place 3.

Elf	Essential items	Intended place	Actual place
Anya Tows	Very Important Maps satchel		3
Hansen Pockets			
Henny Questions		3	
Betty B. Ready	Presents	1	1
Joanna Hand		5	

H. Clue 8 states that the address list ended up closer to the presents than the Christmas sweater. We know that the presents were in Place 1, in the area behind the bench. When we look at the diagram, we can see that Places 2 and 3 are closer to the presents than Places 4 and 5 which are to-

wards the front of the sleigh. Therefore, the address list's actual place must have been either Place 2 or Place 3, and the Christmas sweater's actual place must have been either Place 4 or 5.

We know that Anya Tows packed the Very Important Maps satchel in Place 3. Hence, the address list's actual place cannot have been Place 3, but must have been Place 2.

Essential item: Address list = Actual place: 2
Essential item: Christmas sweater = Actual place: 4 OR 5

I. Clue 4 states that the sum of the intended place numbers where Joanna Hand and Hansen Pockets were supposed to have packed their items was the same as the sum of the compartment numbers where the Very Important Maps satchel and the snacks consisting of carrots and cookies ended up. We know that Joanna Hand's intended place number was 5, and we established in Explanation B that Hansen Pockets' intended place number was either 2 or 4. It follows from this that the sum of Joanna Hand and Hansen Pockets' intended place numbers was either 7 or 9 (that is, 5 + 2 = 7 or 5 + 4 = 9).

We know that the Very Important Maps satchel's actual place was 3. We don't know the actual place number of the carrots and cookies, but we do know that the actual place of the presents was 1 and the actual place of the Very Important Maps satchel was 3. We also established in Explanation H that the actual place of the address list was 2. It follows from this that the carrots and cookies' actual place must have been either 4 or 5. When we calculate the sum of the actual place numbers of the Very Important Maps satchel and the carrots and cookies, we get either 7 or 8 (that is, 3 + 4 = 7 or 3 + 5 = 8).

We have now established that the sum of Joanna Hand and Hansen Pockets' intended place numbers was either 7 or 9, and that the sum of the actual place numbers of the Very Important Maps satchel and the carrots and cookies was either 7 or 8. Since these sums should be the same, we can deduce that both sums must be 7. It follows from this that Hansen Pockets' intended place number must have been 2, and the carrots and cookies' actual place must have been 4.

Essential items: Carrots & cookies = Actual place: 4

Elf	Essential items	Intended place	Actual place
Anya Tows	Very Important Maps satchel		3
Hansen Pockets		2	
Henny Questions		3	
Betty B. Ready	Presents	1	1
Joanna Hand		5	

J. We established in Explanation C that Anya Tows' intended place was either 2 or 4. We now know that Hansen Pockets' intended place was 2. Therefore, Anya Tows' intended place must have been 4.

Elf	Essential items	Intended place	Actual place
Anya Tows	Very Important Maps satchel	4	3
Hansen Pockets		2	
Henny Questions		3	
Betty B. Ready	Presents	1	1
Joanna Hand		5	

K. Clue 5 states that the Christmas sweater ended up in a compartment that had been meant for the address list. In other words, the actual place of the Christmas sweater was the same as the intended place of the address list. We established in Explanation H that the actual place of the Christmas sweater was 4 or 5. Therefore, the intended place of the address list must have been 4 or 5. However, we know that the intended place of the Very Important Maps satchel that was packed by Anya Tows was 4. Therefore, the intended place of the address list must have been 5. This also means that the actual place of the Christmas sweater must have been 5.

We know that Joanna Hand's intended place was 5. It follows from this that it must have been Joanna Hand who packed the address list.

We established in Explanation H that the address list's actual place was 2. We know that Joanna Hand packed the address list. Therefore, she must have packed it in Place 2.

Essential items: Christmas sweater: Actual place: 5

Elf	Essential items	Intended place	Actual place
Anya Tows	Very Important Maps satchel	4	3
Hansen Pockets		2	
Henny Questions		3	
Betty B. Ready	Presents	1	1
Joanna Hand	Address list	5	2

L. Clue 10 indicates that the snacks should have been on the left-hand side of the sleigh. Clue 4 explains that the snacks consisted of carrots and cookies. Hence, it is carrots and cookies whose intended place was on the left-hand side. When we look at the diagram, Places 3 and 5 are on the left-hand side. Therefore, the intended place of the carrots and cookies must have been either in Place 3 or Place 5. However, we know that the address list's intended place was 5. Therefore, the intended place of the carrots and cookies must have been in Place 3. We know that Henny Questions was meant to pack her items in Place 3. Hence, it was Henny Questions who packed the carrots and cookies.

We established in Explanation I that the carrots and cookies' actual place was 4. Therefore, Henny Questions must have actually packed them in Place 4.

Elf	Essential items	Intended place	Actual place
Anya Tows	Very Important Maps satchel	4	3
Hansen Pockets		2	
Henny Questions	Carrots & cookies	3	4
Betty B. Ready	Presents	1	1
Joanna Hand	Address list	5	2

M. We know that Anya Tows ended up packing the Very Important Maps satchel in Place 3, Henny Questions ended up packing the carrots and cookies in Place 4, Betty B. Ready ended up packing the presents in Place 1, and Joanna Hand ended up packing the address list in Place 2. Therefore, it must have been Hansen Pockets who ended up packing the Christmas sweater in Place 5.

Elf	Essential items	Intended place	Actual place
Anya Tows	Very Important Maps satchel	4	3
Hansen Pockets	Christmas sweater	2	5
Henny Questions	Carrots & cookies	3	4
Betty B. Ready	Presents	1	1
Joanna Hand	Address list	5	2

25. A Lost Claus

A. Clue 2 indicates that the problem of slow speed was due to the reindeer being unfit and not able to sustain the speed needed and the sleigh's aerodynamic features not working properly. Clue 15 describes Tinsel Cheeks and her reindeer relieving the slowest of Santa's reindeer and Angie Near tweaking the sleigh's aerodynamic features. We can, therefore, deduce that it was Angie Near and Tinsel Cheeks who helped Santa with the problem of slow speed.

Problem	Place	Order	Help from	Rudolph said...
Damaged wrapping paper				
Getting lost				
Inefficient route planning				
Presents lost				
Slow speed			Angie Near & Tinsel Cheeks	

B. Clue 1 indicates that Santa got lost without the genuine Very Important Maps a few minutes after 11.27 pm. Clue 11 indicates that there were 3 places where Santa faced adversities after midnight, and so he must have

faced 2 problems before midnight. Clue 10 indicates that there was a problem that took place at 11.58 pm. Therefore, we can deduce that getting lost shortly after 11.27 pm must have been Santa's 1st problem, and the problem that took place at 11.58 pm must have been the 2nd problem.

Clue 9 indicates that when Mrs Claus handed the Very Important Maps to Santa, Rudolph said, "The best thing since iced gingerbread!" Clue 9 also indicates that her helper gave Rudolph candy canes from his winter jacket pockets. When we look at the 'Help from' options, we can see that Mrs Claus helped Santa on 2 occasions, once with Brave Dave and once with Professor Knot-a-Lot. Clue 12 indicates that Professor Knot-a-Lot helped Santa after midnight. Since Santa got lost before midnight – shortly after 11.27 pm – Professor Knot-a-Lot can't have helped with this particular problem. It follows from this that it must have been Mrs Claus and Brave Dave who helped Santa when he got lost.

Problem that took place at 11.58 pm = Order: 2nd

Problem	Place	Order	Help from	Rudolph said...
Damaged wrapping paper				
Getting lost		1st	Mrs Claus & Brave Dave	"The best thing since iced gingerbread!"
Inefficient route planning				
Presents lost				
Slow speed			Angie Near & Tinsel Cheeks	

C. Clue 2 states that the reason why presents flew off the sleigh and got lost was because the elf responsible for packing them had not tied the rope knots securely. Clue 4 describes how the 2 helpers found the lost presents with the help of Christmas goggles and then made sure all the presents were tied down using the most secure knots. Clue 12 indicates that Professor Knot-a-Lot's knot expertise was needed when he helped Santa. This is to say that he must have been part of the duo who helped find the lost presents and tie them securely in their place in the sleigh. When we look at the 'Help from' options, there is only 1 partner who formed a duo with Professor Knot-a-Lot: Mrs Claus. Hence, it was Professor Knot-a-Lot and Mrs Claus who helped with the lost presents.

Problem	Place	Order	Help from	Rudolph said...
Damaged wrapping paper				
Getting lost		1st	Mrs Claus & Brave Dave	"The best thing since iced gingerbread!"
Inefficient route planning				
Presents lost			Professor Knot-a-Lot & Mrs Claus	
Slow speed			Angie Near & Tinsel Cheeks	

D. Clue 10 states that Brave Dave was part of the duo that helped Santa at 11.58 pm. We established in Explanation B that Mrs Claus and Brave Dave helped Santa shortly after 11.27 pm. Therefore, Brave Dave must have helped Santa with Miss Tress at 11.58 pm.

We know that Mrs Claus and Brave Dave helped Santa when he got lost, Professor Knot-a-Lot and Mrs Claus helped to find the lost presents, and Angie Near and Tinsel Cheeks helped with the problem of slow speed. Hence, Miss Tress and Brave Dave must have helped Santa either with the damaged wrapping paper or the inefficient route planning. Clue 11 indicates that the problem of damaged wrapping paper occurred after midnight. Since Miss Tress and Brave Dave helped Santa at 11.58 pm, they must have helped with the problem of inefficient route planning.

We established in Explanation B that the problem that took place at 11.58 pm was the 2nd problem. We now know that the problem of inefficient route planning took place at 11.58 pm. Therefore, it must have been the 2nd problem.

Angie Near is female, this isn't expressly mentioned in this puzzle. Therefore, we can't exclude her from the list just yet.)

Clue 14 indicates that the elf with the kangaroo-pouch sweater had a partner who was an elf who lent a hand both before and after midnight. Let's look at the options we listed above, one by one. Angie Near was partnered with Tinsel Cheeks. We know that Tinsel Cheeks is a reindeer and not an elf. Therefore, Angie Near can't be the elf with the kangaroo-pouch sweater. Professor Knot-a-Lot was partnered with Mrs Claus. Since Mrs Claus is not an elf, Professor Knot-a-Lot can't be the elf with the kangaroo-pouch sweater. It follows from this that it must be Elfred Hitchcock who was the elf with the kangaroo-pouch sweater. We know that his partner was Miss Tress, who indeed is an elf. We also know that she helped Santa with the 2nd problem (which took place before midnight, as established in Explanation B) and we now know that she helped Santa after midnight with Elfred Hitchcock.

As mentioned above, Clue 5 states that when Rudolph said, "Apply your elf," he was referring to the elf who wore the kangaroo-pouch Christmas sweater. Now that we know that this elf was Elfred Hitchcock, we can deduce that Rudolph said, "Apply your elf," when Elfred Hitchcock and Miss Tress helped Santa with the damaged wrapping paper.

Elf with the kangaroo-pouch sweater: Elfred Hitchcock

Problem	Place	Order	Help from	Rudolph said...
Damaged wrapping paper			Elfred Hitchcock & Miss Tress	"Apply your elf."
Getting lost		1st	Mrs Claus & Brave Dave	"The best thing since iced gingerbread!"
Inefficient route planning	Banquet Berth	2nd	Miss Tress & Brave Dave	
Presents lost			Professor Knot-a-Lot & Mrs Claus	
Slow speed			Angie Near & Tinsel Cheeks	

H. Clue 8 states that Festival Field was the 2nd place that Santa visited after midnight. We established in Explanation B that there were 2 places that Santa visited before midnight. Therefore, the 2nd place after midnight must have been the 4th place overall. It follows from this that Festival Field must have been the 4th place Santa visited.

Clue 14 states that the elf with the kangaroo-pouch sweater helped Santa after the incident in Festival Field. We established in Explanation G that the elf with the kangaroo-pouch sweater was Elfred Hitchcock. Therefore, it was he and his partner Miss Tress who helped Santa after the incident in Festival Field. We established above that the problem in Festival Field happened 4th. Therefore, Elfred Hitchcock and Miss Tress helped Santa with his 5th problem, and we know that this duo helped with the damaged wrapping paper.

Place: Festival Field = Order: 4th

Problem	Place	Order	Help from	Rudolph said...
Damaged wrapping paper		5th	Elfred Hitchcock & Miss Tress	"Apply your elf."
Getting lost		1st	Mrs Claus & Brave Dave	"The best thing since iced gingerbread!"
Inefficient route planning	Banquet Berth	2nd	Miss Tress & Brave Dave	
Presents lost			Professor Knot-a-Lot & Mrs Claus	
Slow speed			Angie Near & Tinsel Cheeks	

I. Clue 3 states that Miss Tress was part of the duo who helped to solve the problem that made Rudolph exclaim, "We're swimming against the Yuletide." We know that when Miss Tress helped Santa with Elfred Hitchcock, Rudolph said, "Apply your elf." Therefore, it must have been when Miss

---

Problem	Place	Order	Help from	Rudolph said...
Damaged wrapping paper				
Getting lost		1st	Mrs Claus & Brave Dave	"The best thing since iced gingerbread!"
Inefficient route planning		2nd	Miss Tress & Brave Dave	
Presents lost			Professor Knot-a-Lot & Mrs Claus	
Slow speed			Angie Near & Tinsel Cheeks	

E. We know that Mrs Claus and Brave Dave helped Santa when he got lost, Miss Tress and Brave Dave helped to overcome the inefficient route planning, Professor Knot-a-Lot and Mrs Claus helped to find the lost presents, and Angie Near and Tinsel Cheeks helped with the problem of slow speed. Hence, it must have been Elfred Hitchcock and Miss Tress who helped with the damaged wrapping paper.

Problem	Place	Order	Help from	Rudolph said...
Damaged wrapping paper			Elfred Hitchcock & Miss Tress	
Getting lost		1st	Mrs Claus & Brave Dave	"The best thing since iced gingerbread!"
Inefficient route planning		2nd	Miss Tress & Brave Dave	
Presents lost			Professor Knot-a-Lot & Mrs Claus	
Slow speed			Angie Near & Tinsel Cheeks	

F. Clue 1 indicates that Santa got lost immediately before visiting Banquet Berth. We know that Santa got lost 1st. Therefore, Banquet Berth must have been the place where the 2nd problem took place. We know that the 2nd problem was inefficient route planning. Hence, the problem of inefficient route planning happened in Banquet Berth.

Problem	Place	Order	Help from	Rudolph said...
Damaged wrapping paper			Elfred Hitchcock & Miss Tress	
Getting lost		1st	Mrs Claus & Brave Dave	"The best thing since iced gingerbread!"
Inefficient route planning	Banquet Berth	2nd	Miss Tress & Brave Dave	
Presents lost			Professor Knot-a-Lot & Mrs Claus	
Slow speed			Angie Near & Tinsel Cheeks	

G. Clue 5 states that when Rudolph said, "Apply your elf," he was referring to the elf who had filled the kangaroo pouch of his Christmas sweater with candy canes and that Rudolph didn't say this before midnight. We established in Explanation B that the 1st and 2nd problems took place before midnight. Therefore, the elf with a kangaroo pouch Christmas sweater must have been part of one of the duos who helped 3rd, 4th, or 5th. We know that the 1st problem was dealt with by Mrs Claus and Brave Dave, and the 2nd problem was solved by Miss Tress and Brave Dave. When we look at the remaining helpers, the options are: Elfred Hitchcock, Miss Tress, Professor Knot-a-Lot, Mrs Claus, Angie Near, and Tinsel Cheeks. However, Clue 5 indicates that this helper with the sweater that had a kangaroo pouch filled with candy canes was a male elf. This immediately excludes Miss Tress, Mrs Claus, and Tinsel Cheeks (Clue 15 indicates that Tinsel Cheeks is a female reindeer). The remaining elves are Elfred Hitchcock, Professor Knot-a-Lot, and Angie Near. (Although we may remember from a previous puzzle that

Tress helped solve the problem of inefficient route planning with Brave Dave that Rudolph said, "We're swimming against the Yuletide."

Problem	Place	Order	Help from	Rudolph said...
Damaged wrapping paper		5th	Elfred Hitchcock & Miss Tress	"Apply your elf."
Getting lost		1st	Mrs Claus & Brave Dave	"The best thing since iced gingerbread!"
Inefficient route planning	Banquet Berth	2nd	Miss Tress & Brave Dave	"We're swimming against the Yuletide."
Presents lost			Professor Knot-a-Lot & Mrs Claus	
Slow speed			Angie Near & Tinsel Cheeks	

J. Clue 13 states that it was one of the elves with a Christmas sweater that had skis in its sleeves who heard Rudolph say to Santa, "Don't stop be-leaf-ing." We know that Elfred Hitchcock and Miss Tress heard Rudolph say, "Apply your elf."; Mrs Claus and Brave Dave heard Rudolph say, "The best thing since iced gingerbread!"; and Miss Tress and Brave Dave heard Rudolph say, "We're swimming against the Yuletide." Therefore, it was either the duo of Professor Knot-a-Lot and Mrs Claus or the duo of Angie Near and Tinsel Cheeks who heard Rudolph say, "Don't stop be-leaf-ing." while they were solving a problem.

Clue 7 states that there were 2 female elves who wore matching sweaters that had skis in their sleeves. Since Clue 12 indicates that Professor Knot-a-Lot is male, Mrs Claus is not an elf, and Tinsel Cheeks is a reindeer (Clue 15 and Explanation G), the only female elf belonging to the above mentioned 2 duos is Angie Near. Hence, it must have been Angie Near who heard Rudolph say, "Don't stop be-leaf-ing," as she and Tinsel Cheeks helped Santa with the problem of slow speed.

We know that Elfred Hitchcock and Miss Tress heard Rudolph say, "Apply your elf."; Mrs Claus and Brave Dave heard Rudolph say, "The best thing since iced gingerbread!"; Miss Tress and Brave Dave heard Rudolph say, "We're swimming against the Yuletide."; and Angie Near and Tinsel Cheeks heard Rudolph say, "Don't stop be-leaf-ing." Therefore, it must have been Professor Knot-a-Lot and Mrs Claus who heard Rudolph say, "That was too Claus for comfort," as they helped Santa to find the lost presents.

Problem	Place	Order	Help from	Rudolph said...
Damaged wrapping paper		5th	Elfred Hitchcock & Miss Tress	"Apply your elf."
Getting lost		1st	Mrs Claus & Brave Dave	"The best thing since iced gingerbread!"
Inefficient route planning	Banquet Berth	2nd	Miss Tress & Brave Dave	"We're swimming against the Yuletide."
Presents lost			Professor Knot-a-Lot & Mrs Claus	"That was too Claus for comfort."
Slow speed			Angie Near & Tinsel Cheeks	"Don't stop be-leaf-ing."

K. Clue 10 indicates that Brave Dave helped Santa at 11.58 pm and this happened in a place that was visited immediately before Celebration City. We established in Explanation B that the problem that took place at 11.58 pm was the 2nd problem. So, since this 2nd problem took place immediately before the problem in Celebration City, the problem in Celebration City must have happened 3rd.

Clue 6 indicates that it was either in the place immediately before Party Patch or the in the place immediately after Soiree Suburb where Santa had the problem with the inefficient route list. We know that the inefficient route list was the 2nd problem and took place in Banquet Berth. We also established above that this problem took place immediately before the 3rd problem in Celebration City. Therefore, this problem of inefficient route planning in Banquet Berth cannot have taken place immediately be-

fore the problem in Party Patch. It follows from this that the problem in Banquet Berth must have taken place immediately after the problem in Soiree Suburb. Since the problem in Banquet Berth was the 2nd problem, the problem that preceded it must have been the 1st problem – which we know was Santa getting lost. Therefore, we can deduce that Santa got lost in Soiree Suburb.

Place: Celebration City: Order: 3rd

Problem	Place	Order	Help from	Rudolph said...
Damaged wrapping paper		5th	Elfred Hitchcock & Miss Tress	"Apply your elf."
Getting lost	Soiree Suburb	1st	Mrs Claus & Brave Dave	"The best thing since iced gingerbread!"
Inefficient route planning	Banquet Berth	2nd	Miss Tress & Brave Dave	"We're swimming against the Yuletide."
Presents lost			Professor Knot-a-Lot & Mrs Claus	"That was too Claus for comfort."
Slow speed			Angie Near & Tinsel Cheeks	"Don't stop be-leaf-ing."

L. We know that getting lost was the 1st problem and took place in Soiree Suburb, and inefficient route planning was the 2nd problem and took place in Banquet Berth. We established in Explanation H that the 4th problem took place in Festival Field, and we established in Explanation K that the 3rd problem took place in Celebration City. Therefore, we can deduce that the 5th problem must have taken place in Party Patch. We know that the problem of damaged wrapping paper was the 5th problem. Therefore, it must have taken place in Party Patch.

Problem	Place	Order	Help from	Rudolph said...
Damaged wrapping paper	Party Patch	5th	Elfred Hitchcock & Miss Tress	"Apply your elf."
Getting lost	Soiree Suburb	1st	Mrs Claus & Brave Dave	"The best thing since iced gingerbread!"
Inefficient route planning	Banquet Berth	2nd	Miss Tress & Brave Dave	"We're swimming against the Yuletide."
Presents lost			Professor Knot-a-Lot & Mrs Claus	"That was too Claus for comfort."
Slow speed			Angie Near & Tinsel Cheeks	"Don't stop be-leaf-ing."

M. Clue 2 indicates that the presents got lost after Santa's visit to Celebration City. This means that the presents weren't lost in Celebration City. Since the problem of damaged wrapping paper happened in Party Patch, Santa got lost in Soiree Suburb, and the problem of inefficient route planning took place in Banquet Berth, it follows that the presents must have got lost in Festival Field.

We established in Explanation H that Santa's visit to Festival Field was the 4th in order. Since the presents got lost in Festival Field, the lost presents must have been the 4th problem that Santa encountered.

Problem	Place	Order	Help from	Rudolph said...
Damaged wrapping paper	Party Patch	5th	Elfred Hitchcock & Miss Tress	"Apply your elf."
Getting lost	Soiree Suburb	1st	Mrs Claus & Brave Dave	"The best thing since iced gingerbread!"
Inefficient route planning	Banquet Berth	2nd	Miss Tress & Brave Dave	"We're swimming against the Yuletide."
Presents lost	Festival Field	4th	Professor Knot-a-Lot & Mrs Claus	"That was too Claus for comfort."
Slow speed			Angie Near & Tinsel Cheeks	"Don't stop be-leaf-ing."

N. Since the 5th problem of damaged wrapping paper occurred in Party Patch, the 1st problem of getting lost occurred in Soiree Suburb, the 2nd problem of inefficient route planning occurred in Banquet Berth, and the 4th problem of lost presents occurred in Festival Field, it must be slow speed that was the 3rd problem and it must have happened in Celebration City.

Problem	Place	Order	Help from	Rudolph said...
Damaged wrapping paper	Party Patch	5th	Elfred Hitchcock & Miss Tress	"Apply your elf."
Getting lost	Soiree Suburb	1st	Mrs Claus & Brave Dave	"The best thing since iced gingerbread!"
Inefficient route planning	Banquet Berth	2nd	Miss Tress & Brave Dave	"We're swimming against the Yuletide."
Presents lost	Festival Field	4th	Professor Knot-a-Lot & Mrs Claus	"That was too Claus for comfort."
Slow speed	Celebration City	3rd	Angie Near & Tinsel Cheeks	"Don't stop be-leaf-ing."

The Stickipeak Logic Puzzle Challenge
65 logic grid puzzles with detailed solutions

Jamie is spending the summer with Grandma in Stickipeak. As you go through the puzzles and work out their solutions by using pure logic, you'll get to know this quaint little village, its quirky inhabitants, and what really goes on there.

65 logic grid puzzles with step-by-step solutions
Puzzle sizes: 6 mini grids, 7 small grids, 45 standard-sized grids, and 7 large grids
Difficulty levels: from easy to very challenging

Are you ready for the Stickipeak logic puzzle challenge?

www.lusciousbooks.co.uk/stickipeak

You might also like these puzzle books

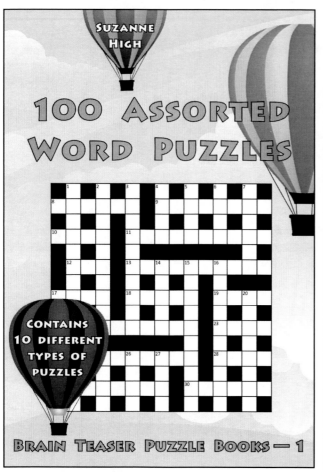

Find out more at
www.lusciousbooks.co.uk

Christmas fun for the whole family

Find out more at
www.lusciousbooks.co.uk

Festive activities for the little ones

Find out more at
www.lusciousbooks.co.uk